My Storybook Dictionary

My Storybook Dictionary

Grolier Incorporated
Danbury, Connecticut

Introduction

Reading is an essential part of living, and adds immeasurably to the richness of your child's life. It is a lifelong source of information and a basic necessity for future success. Reading is also a pleasure for children who have acquired the habit at an early age. It can be a family experience to be shared with your child and can become a memorable part of his or her childhood.

The first part of *My Storybook Dictionary* presents over one thousand entries in a unique and satisfying way. The definitions are often accompanied by examples and analogies, which are easily comprehensible and useful to the young child. The illustrations serve not only to enhance the pages, but to illustrate the definitions as well.

The selection of prose and poetry is from time-proven favorites of children. They have been simplified in vocabulary to allow the beginning reader to enjoy the thrill of reading alone. The words in the dictionary are used over and over again in the literature and will familiarize the child with the vocabulary while providing the adventures of good reading.

As your child reads about *Jack and the Beanstalk* or *Sinbad the Sailor*, a new word can be looked up quickly and easily in the front of this book and yet the child will not be "taken away" from the story. The dictionary is never far away and is always helpful.

A contents page for the STORYBOOK section will be found on page 225.

Contents

HOW TO USE *MY STORYBOOK DICTIONARY*

In the following story, SNOW WHITE AND THE
SEVEN DWARFS, words that are explained in MY
STORYBOOK DICTIONARY are printed in blue.
The story is followed by examples of the definitions of
the words that appear in the first sentence of the story.

Each word definition on pages xiv and xv is also to be
found within the "Dictionary" itself, on the pages indicated. Many other words are also clearly defined,
although not necessarily in the exact form or tense used
in the story. For example, the word "sat" will be found
listed under the word "sit."

So, as you will quickly see by the many words indicated in
blue in this story, MY STORYBOOK DICTIONARY is
ready to help your child with simple and attractive word
explanations when they are needed. And when your
child needs no help, the story will move swiftly and
happily to a satisfying finale.

SNOW WHITE AND THE SEVEN DWARFS

One winter's day, a gentle Queen sat by
her window sewing. As she sewed she
cut her finger. Two little drops of blood
fell from it.

The Queen made a wish. "How I wish
for a little daughter with cheeks as rosy
as those drops of blood. May her skin be
white as snow. May her hair be black as
night."

To the Queen's great joy, her wish
came true. She had a little daughter and
named her Snow White.

Soon after this the Queen died. The
King married another lady. She was

very beautiful but very unkind. And every day she looked into her magic mirror and asked:

"Mirror, mirror, on the wall,
Who is the fairest of them all?"

The mirror would say:

"You, Queen, are fairest of them all."

The years passed. Snow White grew into a very lovely girl. One day the Queen looked into the mirror. To her great surprise it said:

"Fair and lovely though you are,
Snow White fairer is by far."

This made the Queen very angry. She called her servants. "Kill Snow White," she said. But the servants loved Snow White. They did not want to kill her. So one took her into the forest. He left her there and hoped that somebody would find her and take care of her.

Snow White walked alone in the forest. Then she came to a little cottage. She opened the door and went in. She found seven little beds, seven little glasses of wine, and seven loaves of bread. She ate a good dinner. Then she lay down and fell fast asleep.

This cottage belonged to seven dwarfs. When it was dark they came home and lit their seven lamps. Then they found Snow White.

"How beautiful she is!" they all said.

At this Snow White sat up in bed.

"Do not be afraid," said the dwarfs. "We are your friends. But, tell us, how did you come here?"

So Snow White told them her story

and the dwarfs said she could live with them.

"But," they said, "be careful. Keep the door locked while we are away. The Queen may find you and try to hurt you."

And the Queen did find out where Snow White was. She dressed herself up as an old woman. She went to the cottage. Soon Snow White heard somebody calling: "Fine things to sell! Fine things to sell!"

Snow White opened the window and looked out. She saw the old woman selling very pretty ribbons and laces. So she forgot what the dwarfs had said. She unlocked the door and ran out.

"I think I will buy some ribbons!" she said.

"Let me put them on your dress for you," said the old woman. Then she tied them very tight. Snow White fell down as if she were dead.

"That is the end of your beauty," said the Queen.

Soon the dwarfs came home. They saw Snow White and guessed what had happened. Quick as can be, one of them took out a knife. He cut the ribbons. In a few minutes Snow White was better.

When the Queen got back to the palace she went to her room. She took off the old woman's clothes. She put on a fine gown and a beautiful necklace. Then she looked into her magic mirror and asked:

"Mirror, mirror, on the wall,
Who is the fairest of them all?"

Much to her surprise the mirror said:

"Fair and lovely though you are,
Snow White fairest is by far."

So the Queen knew that Snow White was still alive. And she began to make another plan to kill her.

The seven dwarfs went away the next morning. They told Snow White again not to open the door to anyone.

The same morning the Queen painted her face. She dressed as a poor woman and went to the cottage. This time she took a beautiful apple. One side of it was filled with poison.

"Would you like this pretty apple?" she said. She held it up so Snow White could see it.

But Snow White was wiser now. She would not take it.

"Do you think it is poisoned?" said the old woman. "See I shall eat part of it. That will show you it is good." And she took a bite from the side that was all right.

The apple looked beautiful. The old woman had eaten some of it. So Snow White held out her hand. She put the apple to her lips. But as soon as she took a bite she fell down on the floor.

Then the Queen went back to the palace. She asked her magic mirror:

"Mirror, mirror, on the wall,
  Who is the fairest of them all?"

This time the mirror said:

"Thou, Queen, art fairest of
  them all."

Then the Queen knew that Snow White was dead at last.

At dusk the dwarfs went back to the cottage. But they could not help Snow White. She was dead. Sadly they put her in a glass box. They set it on a hill for everyone to see

One day a Prince was passing by. When he saw Snow White, he loved her at once. So he gave the dwarfs a lot of money to let him carry her box away. But as it was being lifted, one of the men carrying the box fell The door of the box flew open The piece of apple fell out of Snow White's mouth She sat up at once.

The Prince was full of joy to find that she was still alive. He had heard the story of the Queen from the dwarfs.

Snow White gave the Prince her hand. She went away with him to his father's palace. They were married and lived happily ever after.

The Queen was invited to the wedding. But she was so angry that Snow White was alive that she fell down in a fit and died.

EXAMPLES

one
(page 131)

➥ **One** is a number. **One** is also written as **1.** Here is **one** pineapple.

orange

---

winter
(page 214)

➥ **Winter** is one of the four seasons of the year. **Winter** is the coldest season of the year. When the **winter** is very cold, rain turns to snow, and water in lakes and rivers turns to ice.

---

day
(page 49)

➥ A **day** is the **night and the day together.** A **day** is twenty-four hours long. There are seven **days** in a week. The **days** of the week are Sunday, Monday, Tuesday, Wednesday, Thursday, Friday, and Saturday.

a
(page 1)

➡ I have **a** father and **an** uncle.
I have **one** father and **one** uncle.

---

by
(page 31)

➡ I was hit **by** a ball.
I was hit **with** a ball.

➡ The puppy stayed **by** its mother.
The puppy stayed **near** its mother.

➡ We drove **by** their house.
We drove **past** their house.

➡ I go to school **by** bus.
I go to school **using** a bus.

➡ We must be at the movies **by** six o'clock.
We must be at the movies **no later than** six
o'clock.

➡ Terry was kissed **by** her mother. Terry's mother
kissed her.

---

sew (page 163) ➡ To **sew** means to **put thread through** two things
to hold them together.
I **sewed** a button on my shirt. I **put thread
through** the button and the shirt to hold
them together.

---

xv

My Dictionary

A a

a ➡️ I have **a** father and **an** uncle.
I have **one** father and **one** uncle.

---

able ➡️ To be **able** means you **can** do something.
I **am able** to reach that shelf.
I **can** reach that shelf.

---

about ➡️ The story is **about** Sleeping Beauty.
The story is **of** Sleeping Beauty.

➡️ The puppies ran **about** the floor.
The puppies ran **all over** the floor.

➡️ I have **about** nine marbles.
I have **close to** nine marbles.

➡️ She is **about** seven years old.
She is **almost** seven years old.

---

above ➡️ The bird flew **above** the trees.
The bird flew **over** the trees.
The bird flew **higher** than the trees.

1

across

➡️Why did the chicken run **across** the road?

To get **to the other side.**

---

act

➡️To **act** is to **do** anything.
These are some **acts** you do every day:

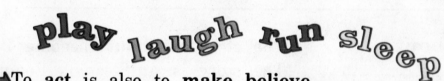

➡️To **act** is also to **make believe.**
He's not really ill. He's just **acting**.

➡️To **act** is also to **play a part** in a play.
She **acted the part** of Peter Pan in the school play.

---

add

➡️To **add** is to **put numbers together.**
Two **added** to four make six.

$$2+4=6$$

The sign + means to **add.**

➡️To **add** is to **put things together.**
Add water to dirt to make mud.

address

Your **address** is the **place where you live.** It tells the mailman where to bring your mail. It tells your friends where to visit you. Your **address** shows

the **number of your house or building**
the **name or number of your street**
the **name of your town or city**
the **name of the state you live in.**

Carol Bryant
12 Main Street
Central, Iowa 12345

afraid

Afraid means being worried about something you think can hurt you.
I'm **afraid** to cross the highway.

after

After means **to follow.**
Ten comes **after** nine.

She was running **after** her dog.
She was running **behind** her dog.

Timmy goes to bed **after** his baby brother.
Timmy goes to bed **later** than his baby brother.

afternoon

Jill eats lunch at twelve o'clock noon.
Jill eats dinner in the evening.
She has a snack **between lunch and dinner.**
She has a snack in the **afternoon.**

again　　　➡Again means to happen **another time.**
　　　　　　　It rained yesterday. It rained **again** today.

---

against　　➡The broom is leaning **against** the wall. The top
　　　　　　　of the broom is touching the wall. The bottom of
　　　　　　　the broom is away from the wall.

　　　　　　　➡The friends played baseball
　　　　　　　　　　against each other.
　　　　　　　The friends played baseball
　　　　　　　　on two different teams.

　　　　　　　➡I am **against** hurting animals.
　　　　　　　I **do not like** hurting animals.

---

age　　　➡Your **age** is how **old** you are.
　　　　　　What is your **age?**
　　　　　　I am six years of **age.**

　6　　　How **old** are you?
　　　　　　I am six years **old.**

---

ago　　　➡Ago means that something **happened in the
　　　　　past.**
　　　　　　My balloon broke. How long **ago** was that?
　　　　　　That was two hours **ago.**

---

air　　　➡Air is what you breathe through your nose and
　　　　　mouth. You cannot see it or smell it or taste it.
　　　　　Birds and airplanes fly through the **air.**

airplane

An **airplane** is a machine with wings that can fly through the air. An **airplane** is driven by propellers or jets. A place where **airplanes** take off and land is called an airport.

alive

This tree is **alive.**
This tree is **living.** It can make leaves and flowers and fruit.

This tree is **not alive.**
This tree is **dead.** It cannot make leaves and flowers and fruit.

all

We ate **all** of the cupcakes.
We ate **every one** of the cupcakes.

I have done **all** of my homework.
I have done **every bit** of my homework.

Jimmy worked on the puzzle **all** afternoon.
Jimmy worked on the puzzle the **whole** afternoon.

alligator

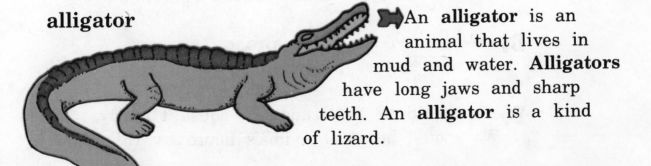

An **alligator** is an animal that lives in mud and water. **Alligators** have long jaws and sharp teeth. An **alligator** is a kind of lizard.

almost

almost ➡️ Tom is seven years old. Joan is six-and-a-half years old. Joan is **almost** as old as Tom.
Joan is **nearly** as old as Tom.

---

alone ➡️ **Alone** means **being by yourself.**
She lived **alone** in the big old house.
She lived **with no one** in the big old house.

➡️ Anne **alone** had the right answer. **Only** Anne had the right answer.

---

along ➡️ Cars were parked all **along** the street.
Cars were parked **from one end of the street to the other end** of the street.

➡️ The parade marched **along.**
The parade marched **forward.**

---

alphabet ➡️ These are the 26 letters of the **alphabet.**

Aa Bb Cc Dd Ee Ff Gg Hh Ii

Jj Kk Ll Mm Nn Oo Pp Qq Rr

Ss Tt Uu Vv Ww Xx Yy Zz

---

already ➡️ I have eaten my lunch **already.**
I have eaten my lunch **before this time.**

➡️ Are the cookies baked **already?**
Are the cookies baked **so soon?**

➡️ We should be at Grandma's house **already.**
We should be at Grandma's house **by this time.**

6

also
➪ Linda has a dog. Linda has a turtle **also**.
Linda has a turtle **too**.

➪ Karen lives next door. She is **also** my friend.
Karen lives next door **and** she is my friend.

---

although
➪ **Although** Allen was nasty to me yesterday, I still like him.
➪ **Even though** Allen was nasty to me yesterday, I still like him.

➪ Eileen went to school today, **although** she felt ill.
Eileen went to school today, **but** she felt ill.

---

always
➪ A pine tree **always** keeps its leaves.
A pine tree **at all times** keeps it leaves.

➪ On my birthday I **always** have a birthday cake. Every birthday I have a birthday cake.

---

am
➪ I **am** happy.　　We **are** happy.
You **are** happy.　You **are** happy.
He **is** happy.　　They **are** happy.
She **is** happy.　　**Are** you happy?

---

among
➪ The house stood **among** tall trees.
The house has tall trees **all around** it.

➪ There is a book **among** my toys.
There is a book **mixed with** my toys.

➪ The three mice shared the cheese **among** themselves. Each mouse had some cheese.

an   ⇨I have **an** aunt and **a** mother.
I have **one** aunt and **one** mother.

⇨I saw **an** airplane, but it was not the **one** I saw yesterday.

and   ⇨Randy **and** I have the same birthday. Randy's birthday is on March 9. My birthday is on March 9 too.

⇨One **and** one are two.
One **added** to one are two.
One **plus** one are two.

animal   ⇨An **animal** is a living thing that moves and eats and breathes. These are some **animals.**

Can you name some other **animals?**

ankle   ⇨Your **ankle** is the part of your body between your leg and your foot.

another   ⇨I have eaten one sandwich. I am still hungry.
I would like **another** sandwich.
I would like **one more** sandwich.

⇨My pen has run out of ink.
May I have **another** pen?
May I have **a different** pen?

answer

To **answer** means to say something when asked a question.

> I asked him, "What time is it?"
> He **answered,** "It is two o'clock."

To **answer** is to find out who is calling when the telephone rings. To **answer** also means to see who is at the door when the doorbell rings.

An **answer** is what you say when you are asked a question.

> "How much are two and five?
> "The **answer** is seven."

---

ant

An **ant** is a very small animal. It is also called an insect or a bug. There are many different kinds of **ants.** An **ant** may be black or red in color. Some **ants** live in nests in the ground. Other **ants** live in wood.

---

any

Do you have **any** popcorn?
Do you have **some** popcorn?

I want that bicycle, not just **any** bicycle.

---

apart

One house stood **apart** from the others.
There were no other houses near it.

When I dropped my wristwatch, it fell **apart.**
When I dropped my wristwatch, it broke into many parts.

apartment

An **apartment** is a home in a building. Many families live in the building. Each family has its own rooms. Sharon's **apartment** has a living room, a dining room, a kitchen, a bathroom, and two bedrooms.

ape

An **ape** is an animal that is like a monkey, but an **ape** has no tail. Chimpanzees and gorillas are **apes.**

appear

To **appear** is to **be seen.**
When the moon rises it **appears** above the trees.
When the moon rises it **can be seen** above the trees.

To **appear** is also to look like something.
Wayne is smiling. He **appears** happy.
    He **seems** happy.

apple

An **apple** is a red or green or yellow fruit that grows on a tree. You can eat an **apple** raw. You can eat an **apple** cooked in an **apple** pie. **Apple** trees have pink or white flowers.

are ➤ Where **are** we? We **are** in the kitchen. What **are** we doing? We **are** making sandwiches.

➤ Who **are** they? They **are** my friends from school.

➤ What **are** these? They **are** oranges.

---

arm ➤ Your **arm** is the part of your body between your shoulder and your hand.

➤ When a part of something is for your **arm,** it is called an **arm.**
This chair has **arms.**

This chair has no **arms.**

My sweater has a hole in one **arm.**

---

army ➤ An **army** is a large group of soldiers.
The king marched with his **army.**

---

around ➤ The tree has a fence **around** it.
The tree has a fence that **circles** it.

➤ It is **around** dinnertime.
It is **about** dinnertime.

---

arrow ➤ An **arrow** is a stick with a sharp point at one end and feathers at the other end. An **arrow** is what you shoot from a bow.

ONE WAY

➤ An **arrow** is also a sign pointing in a direction.

11

art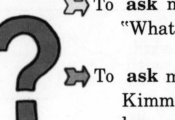

➡ **Art** is drawing and painting and making statues.

➡ **Art** is also what you call the pictures and statues.

➡ An **art** is something that is done very well. Dancing, cooking, playing musical instruments, and sewing are **arts.**

---

as

➡ **As** I walk along I hum to myself.
While I walk along I hum to myself.

➡ I am **as big as** my sister. My sister and I are the **same size.**

➡ It gets light **as** the sun rises.
It gets light **when** the sun rises.

---

ask

➡ To **ask** means to say a question.
"What is your name?" she **asks.**

➡ To **ask** means also to say you want something. Kimmie would like some ice cream. She **asks** her mother for some ice cream. She says, "Mother, may I have some ice cream?"

➡ To **ask** means to say you want someone to come. She **asked** him to her birthday party. She wanted him to come to her birthday party.

---

asleep

➡ Jean is very tired. She gets into bed and closes her eyes. She falls **asleep.**
Jean is **asleep.**
Jean is **sleeping.**
Jean is **not awake.**

astronaut ⇨ An **astronaut** is a person who travels in a spaceship. American **astronauts** have landed on the moon.

at ⇨ John pointed **at** the cat.
John pointed **in the direction** of the cat.

⇨ Paul asked, "Are we going out for dinner?" "No, we are having dinner **at** home," replied Mother. Paul then asked, "**At** what time will dinner be ready?" Mother said, "Dinner will be ready **at** five o'clock."

ate ⇨ This morning I **ate** cereal and toast for breakfast. It was very good. I **ate** all of it. Now I am eating a peanut butter and jelly sandwich. When I have eaten my sandwich I will eat a banana.

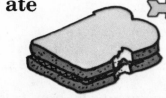

aunt ⇨ Your **aunt** is your mother's sister. Your **aunt** is your father's sister. An **aunt** is also the woman who is married to your uncle.

13

automobile An **automobile** is a machine with a motor and four wheels. We can sit in it and make it go many places. An **automobile** is also called a **car**.

autumn **Autumn** is one of the four seasons of the year. It is the time between summer, when it is warm, and winter, when it is cold. **Autumn** is also called **fall**.

avenue An **avenue** is a wide street.

awake To be **awake** means to **not be asleep**.
Are you asleep? No, I am **awake.**

To **awake** means to stop sleeping.
At what time will you **awake?**
At what time will you **wake up?**

away They went **away** on vacation.
They went **to another place** on vacation. They did not stay home.

ax  An **ax** is a tool used for cutting wood. It has two parts. One part is made of heavy metal and is very sharp. This is the part that cuts. The other part is long and made of wood. This part is called a handle. You hold an **ax** by its handle.

B b

baby

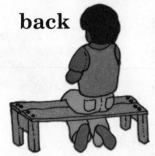

→ A **baby** is a **very young child**.
Peter has a **baby** brother. The **baby** is just six months old.

---

back

→ Your **back** is the part of your body opposite your front. Your **back** goes from your shoulders to your waist.
Gary's red vest keeps his **back** warm.

An animal has a **back** also. A saddle fits over a pony's **back.**

→ The **back** of something is opposite,
or at the other end of, its front.
A caboose is at the **back**
of a train.

→ To go **back** means the opposite
of to go forward.
A swing goes **back** and forward.

→ To go **back** also means to **return.**
Kevin puts his toys **back** on the shelf.
Kevin **returns** his toys to the shelf.

bad

➡ **Bad** means **not good.**
The milk tastes **bad.** The milk is **not good** to drink.

---

bag

➡ A **bag** is a kind of container. A **bag** makes it easier to carry things.
We save the paper **bags** from the grocery store. We use them again as garbage **bags.**

---

bake

➡ To **bake** means to **cook** something in an oven. We are going to **bake** some cookies. The cookies are in the oven. The cookies are **baking.**

---

ball

➡ A **ball** is a plaything that you can throw, catch, hit, or kick. Most balls are round.

➡ A **ball** is also **any round shape or thing.**
Michael made a **ball** of mud.
Michael made a **round shape** with the mud.

---

balloon

➡ A **balloon** is something that gets bigger when you blow air into it. When it is filled with a special kind of air, called helium, it will float up. **Balloons** come in many colors, shapes, and sizes. There are very big **balloons** which can carry people through the air.

banana  A **banana** is a kind of fruit. It is yellow and has a thick skin. **Bananas** grow on trees in warm places.

---

band A **band** is a **group** of people.
Here comes the **band** of robbers!
Here comes the **gang** of robbers!

A **band** is also a group of **musicians.**
A good parade always has a **band.** The music the **band** plays makes it fun to march in the parade.

A **band** is also a **thin strip** of something.
This is a **hatband.**
These are rubber **bands.**

---

bang A **bang** is a **big loud noise.**
When a balloon breaks, it goes **BANG!**

bank  A **bank** is a **place to keep money.**
"Mom and Dad keep their money in a big building called a **bank,** " said Richard. "I keep my money in my little piggy **bank.**

A **bank** is also the edge of a river or stream.
Sarah sat on the **bank** of the river while she was fishing.

barn

barn

↪ A **barn** is a building on a farm. A farmer keeps many things in a **barn**. A farmer keeps animals, food for the animals, and tools in a **barn**.

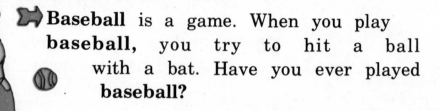

baseball

↪ **Baseball** is a game. When you play **baseball,** you try to hit a ball with a bat. Have you ever played **baseball?**

basket

↪ A **basket** is a kind of container. You can carry things in a **basket**.
Here is a little yellow **basket**.

basketball

↪ **Basketball** is a game. Two teams play this game. The team which gets the ball into the basket the most times is the winner.

bat

↪ A **bat** is what you use to hit a baseball.

↪ To **bat** is to **hit** a ball with a bat.

↪ A **bat** is also a small furry animal. A **bat** can fly, but it is not a bird. **Bats** like dark places. Some **bats** eat insects. Some **bats** eat fruit.

18

bath

Henry is going to **take a bath.** Henry is going to **bathe.** Henry is going to **wash all of his body.** Henry goes into the bathroom and fills the bathtub with warm water. He sits in the bathtub and **washes his whole body.** Henry is **bathing.**

---

be

I **am** Jo Ann. I **am** seven years old. Peter **is** my friend. He **is** seven years old today. Today **is** Peter's birthday. Patricia **is** my friend. She **is** also seven years old today. Peter and Patricia **are** brother and sister. They **are** both seven years old today. Peter, Patricia, and I **are** friends. Now we **are** all seven years old.

I **am**	we **are**
you **are**	you **are**
she **is**	they **are**
he **is**	
it **is**	

---

beach

A **beach** is the flat piece of land that goes to the edge of the sea or a lake. A **beach** is made of sand and pebbles. When it is warm, people like to sit on the **beach.**

---

bean

A **bean** is a kind of vegetable. It is the seed of a plant. **Beans** grow in a case called a pod. **Beans** come in many colors. They are good to eat.

bear   A **bear** is a large furry animal. **Bears** may be black, brown, or white. They have short tails. Some **bears** eat berries. Other **bears** eat fish. Some **bears** also eat honey. A very young **bear** is called a cub.

beard   A **beard** is the hair on the lower part of a man's face. A man can let his **beard** grow or he can shave it off. Do you know someone with a **beard?**

beat   To **beat** means to **hit.**
"When I **beat** my drum," said Danny, "it goes boom, boom, boom."

When Mother makes a cake, she **beats** the eggs. To **beat** the eggs, Mother **stirs very quickly.**

To **beat** also means to **win.**
I **beat** my father at checkers. I **won.** Father lost.

beautiful   **Beautiful** means **very pretty.** We like things that are **beautiful.**

because   **Because** tells why.
I dropped the plate **because** it was hot. Why did you drop the plate? It was hot!

bed

A **bed** is what you sleep on. The room where your **bed** is kept is called a bedroom. When you are tired, it is time for you to go to **bed.** When you are tired, it is bedtime.

bee

A **bee** is a fuzzy insect that has wings you can see through. A **bee** buzzes when it flies. **Bees** live together in a house called a hive. They make honey and keep it in their hive. A **bee** can sting you.

before

One comes **before** all the other numbers.

1 2 3 4 5

Maureen awakes **before** her brother.
Maureen awakes **earlier** than her brother.

Gloria danced **before** her family.
Gloria danced **in front of** her family.

begin

To **begin** means to **start.**
Let's **begin** the game. Let's **start** the game.

The game is **beginning.** The game is **starting.**
The game has **begun.** The game has **started.**

The game **began** ten minutes ago.
The game **started** ten minutes ago.

I am a **beginner.** I have never played this game before this time.

21

behind

behind

The sun is **behind** the cloud.
The sun is **in back of** the cloud.

---

bell

A **bell** is a kind of musical instrument. Some **bells** are shaped like cups. Other .**bells** are round. When a **bell** makes a sound, we say that it rings. Have you ever heard church **bells** ringing on Sunday?

When the **doorbell** rings, you know someone has come to visit you.

These are little jingle **bells.**

---

below

Your mouth is just **below** your nose.
Your mouth is just **under** your nose.
Your nose is over your mouth.

---

bench

A **bench** is a kind of chair. It is big enough for more than one person. A **bench** is usually made of wood.

A workbench is a high, long table. You can stand at the workbench while you hammer and saw.

---

best

I like pears and apples, but I like peaches **best.** I like peaches more than I like pears or apples.

better   ➤Louise is **better** at spelling than Lisa. Lisa is not as good at spelling as Louise.

➤Neil was sick yesterday. Today he is **better.** Neil is not as sick today as he was yesterday.

---

between   ➤Amy sat **between** her mother and her father. Amy sat **in the middle.** Amy's mother was on one side and her father was on the other side.

➤Who ate the sandwich? We divided the sandwich **between** the two of us. We each ate half a sandwich.

---

bicycle   ➤A **bicycle** has two wheels. You sit on a **bicycle** and make it go by pushing the pedals with your feet. A **bicycle** is also called a **bike.**

big   ➤Big means **not small.**
Big means **large.**
The red ball is small. The yellow ball is **bigger** than the red ball. The blue ball is the **biggest** of the three.

bird

A **bird** is an animal with wings and feathers. Most **birds** can fly. An ostrich is a large **bird** that can't fly. Some **birds** can sing. A canary is a **bird** with a beautiful song. A hummingbird is a very small, colorful **bird.**

birthday

Kimmie's **birthday** is January 28. On January 28 she was five years old. Next year, on January 28, she will be six years old. Everybody has a **birthday** once a year. When is your **birthday?**

black

Black is a color. This is **black**. Some people have **black** skin.

blanket

A **blanket** is a large piece of cloth. When you go to sleep you cover yourself with a **blanket.** The **blanket** keeps you warm. This **blanket** is orange.

block

A **block** is fun to play with. **Blocks** are made of wood and have six sides. Some **blocks** have letters or pictures on them.

  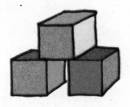

A **block** is also the **street** you live on.
Helen and I live on the same **block.**
Helen and I live on the same **street.**

To **block** means to **stop something from getting through.**
Snow **blocked** the street. There was so much snow on the street that cars could not ride on it.

---

blood

Blood is a liquid inside your body. Your heart keeps the **blood** moving through your body. When you cut yourself, red **blood** comes out. When **blood** comes out, you are bleeding.

---

blue

Blue is a color. This is **blue.**
The sky is **blue.**

Blue also means **sad.**

---

board

A **board** is a **flat piece of wood.** Have you ever hammered a nail into a **board?**

boat

 A **boat** floats in water. You can sit in a **boat** and go for a ride on a lake or on the ocean. **Boats** can be driven by oars, or by sails, or by a motor. A big **boat** is called a ship. Have you ever gone for a ride in a **boat?**

body

Your **body** is **all the parts** of you. Your hand and your knee are parts of your **body.** Can you name some other parts of your **body?**

A **body** is also **all the parts** of an animal.

bone

 A **bone** is a **hard part of your body.** You can feel the **bone** in your elbow, but you cannot see it. Animals have **bones** also.

book

We read **books** to learn about things. All **books** are made of pieces of paper called pages, which are held together at one end. You are looking at a page. This page has words and pictures on it. **Books** also have covers.

 You are reading a **book** now. This kind of **book** is called a dictionary. There are many other kinds of **books.** Do you have any other **books?** Which one do you like the best?

boot

 A **boot** is something you wear on your foot. **Boots** are bigger than shoes. **Boots** keep your feet warmer than shoes do. When it rains, rubber **boots** keep your feet dry.

born ➡ I have a new baby sister. She was **born** this morning. She was **brought into the world** this morning. I did not have a sister yesterday.

---

both ➡ **Both** means **two**.
 Both of my hands are cold. My **two** hands are cold.

---

bottle  ➡ A **bottle** is a kind of container. It is usually made of glass or plastic. Some things that we drink are kept in **bottles.**
 My baby brother drinks milk from a **bottle.**

---

bowl ➡ A **bowl** is a **deep dish.** Most **bowls** are round. I eat my cereal from a **bowl.**

box ➡ A **box** is a kind of container. A **box** has a top, a bottom, and four sides. When you have cereal for breakfast, do you pour it from a **box?**

---

boy ➡ A **boy** is a **young person.** Harry is a **boy.** When he grows up he will be a man. Harry's father is a man.

branch ➥ A **branch** is a part of a tree. Leaves grow from the **branch** of a tree. Sometimes, birds make nests on tree **branches.**

---

brave ➥ Being **brave** means doing something even though you are afraid.

---

bread ➥ **Bread** is a food. To make **bread,** you mix flour with other things and shape it into a loaf. The loaf is baked in an oven. **Bread** is used to make sandwiches.

---

break ➥ To **break** means to make something **come apart in pieces.**

"Did you **break** the window?" asked Mother. "Yes, I **broke** the window with a ball," said Kenny. "I'm sorry the window is **broken.** May I help fix it?"

➥ To **break** also means to make something **stop working.**

I **broke** the radio. The radio is **broken.**
The radio **stopped working.**

---

bridge ➥ A **bridge** is what you walk on to cross a river without getting your feet wet. Cars can drive over big **bridges.** Have you ever been across a **bridge?**

bright

➡ **Bright** means **shiny** or **very light**.
When the sun shines, it is very **bright**.

➡ **Bright** also means **pretty and cheerful**.
The garden was **bright** with flowers.

➡ **Bright** also means **smart**.
Some people are **brighter** than others.

---

brother

➡ Your **brother** is a boy or man who has the same mother and father as you. Do you have a **brother?** What is his name?

---

brown

➡ **Brown** is a color. This is **brown**
Some people have **brown** hair.

---

bubble

➡ A **bubble** is a ball of air. You can blow a **bubble** with **bubble** gum. You can also blow soap **bubbles,** which will float.

---

bug

➡ A **bug** is a very small animal. A **bug** is the same as an **insect.** Butterflies are **bugs** that fly. Ants are **bugs** that walk. Grasshoppers are **bugs** that hop. Fleas are **bugs** that bite.

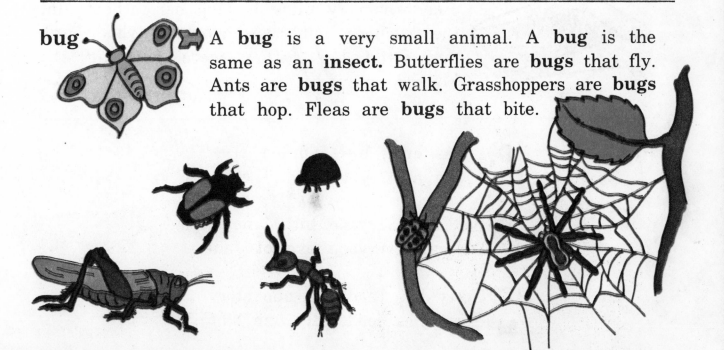

build

To **build** means to **put something together.**
What are you going to **build**?
What are you going to **put together**? I am **building** a treehouse. When will it be all **put together**? It will be **built** by tomorrow.

bulb

An electric light **bulb** is made of glass. It has wires inside. When electricity passes through the wires, they glow. This makes the **bulb** light up.

bus

A **bus** is like an automobile, but it is much bigger. A **bus** has room for many people to ride in it. Do you ride a **bus** to school?

busy

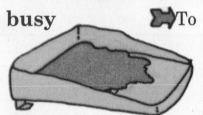

To be **busy** means to be **working.**
Judy was very **busy** helping her father paint the kitchen. Judy was **working** very hard. Judy and her father were painting the kitchen.

but

I was hurt, **but** I didn't cry.
I was hurt, **yet** I didn't cry.

We saw everyone **but** Jane.
We saw everyone **except** Jane.

Gerry has read **but** one story.
Gerry has read **only** one story.

butterfly

➡️ A **butterfly** is an insect with a small body and four big wings. Most **butterflies** have wings of many beautiful colors.

button

➡️ A **button** is used to close a shirt or coat. **Buttons** come in many shapes, colors, and sizes. Are you wearing any **buttons** today? How many **buttons** are you wearing? What colors are they?

buy

➡️ To **buy** means to **get something for money**.
I can **buy** a chocolate bar for 15 cents.

by

➡️ I was hit **by** a ball.
I was hit **with** a ball.

➡️ The puppy stayed **by** its mother.
The puppy stayed **near** its mother.

➡️ We drove **by** their house.
We drove **past** their house.

➡️ I go to school **by** bus.
I go to school **using** a bus.

➡️ We must be at the movies **by** six o'clock.
We must be at the movies **no later than** six o'clock.

➡️ Terry was kissed **by** her mother. Terry's mother kissed her.

cake

➤ **Cake** is a sweet food made with flour, sugar, eggs, and butter. **Cake** is baked in an oven. **Cakes** come in different colors and flavors. Do you have **cake** on your birthday?

---

call

➤ To **call** means to **give a name** to someone or something.
　　They are **calling** the baby Janet.
　　They are **naming** the baby Janet.

➤ To **be called something** means to **have a name.**
　　What is your new pet **called?**
　　My new pet's **name** is Cappy.

➤ To **call** means to **speak on the telephone.**
　　Who is Craig **calling?** Craig is **speaking on the telephone** to his friend Bob.

➤ To **call** means to **speak in a loud voice.**
　　"Help!" **called** Cindy.
　　"Help!" **shouted** Cindy.

camel 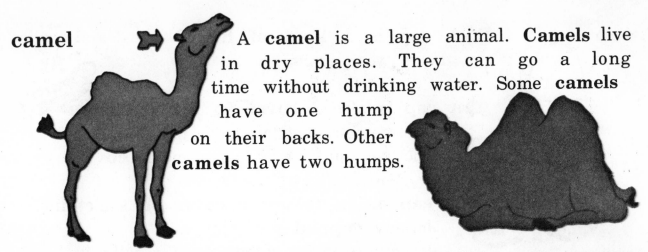 A **camel** is a large animal. **Camels** live in dry places. They can go a long time without drinking water. Some **camels** have one hump on their backs. Other **camels** have two humps.

---

camp ⇒ A **camp** is a place in the country where you live in a tent and are outside all the time.
Some children go to **camp** in the summer.

⇒ To **camp** means to make a place to stay outside for awhile.
We made our **camp** under some trees. We set up a tent and started a fire. Then we ate dinner. Later we went to sleep in the tent.

---

can ⇒ **Can** means **to be able** to do something.
Emily **can** ride a bike.
Emily **is able** to ride a bike.

⇒ A **can** is a metal container. You can buy **cans** of food at the grocery store.

---

candy  ⇒ **Candy** is something sweet to eat. **Candies** come in different shapes, colors, and flavors. **Candy** may be hard or soft or sticky.

cap

➤ A **cap** is a **kind of hat.** Nurses and police officers wear **caps.**

➤ A **cap** is also a **cover** for anything. The ketchup bottle has a metal **cap.** The ketchup bottle has a metal **cover.**

➤ To **cap** means to **put a cover on** something. Jeremy **capped** the jelly jar. Jeremy **put the cover on** the jelly jar.

---

car

➤ A **car** is a machine with a motor and four wheels. A **car** is used to take people and things from one place to another. A **car** is also called an **automobile.**

➤ Railroad **cars** are parts of a train. The engine of the train can pull many **cars.**

care

➤ To take **care** of means to **look after** someone or something. When I was sick, Mother took **care** of me. Mother did many things to make me feel better.

➤ To **care** for means to **like** something. Does Andy **care** for oranges? Yes, Andy **likes** oranges.

---

carriage

➤ A **carriage** is what a baby rides in before it knows how to walk. A **carriage** has four wheels and a place for a baby to sleep. You push a **carriage** to make it move.

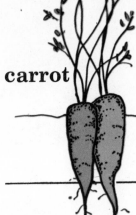

carrot　➡️ A **carrot** is a vegetable. The orange part is called a root because it grows under the ground. The root of the **carrot** is the part we eat. Rabbits also eat **carrots.**

carry　➡️ To **carry** means to **hold something and take it somewhere.**

I **carry** my books to school.
I **take** my books to school.

cat　➡️ A **cat** is a small furry animal. Some families have a pet **cat.** A **cat** says "meow" when it is hungry and purrs when it is happy. A young **cat** is called a kitten.

catch　➡️ To **catch** means to **get hold of something that is moving.**

Jeff said to Kay, "When I throw the ball, you **catch** it." Kay was **able to get hold** of the ball. Kay **caught** the ball.

cent　➡️ A **cent** is a piece of money.　A **cent** is the same as a **penny.** It is also written as **1¢.** Ten **cents** make a dime. One hundred **cents** make a dollar.

center　➡️ The **center** is the **middle** of something.
This doughnut has a hole in the **center.**
This doughnut has a hole in the **middle.**

certain

➡ **Certain** means the same as **sure**.
I am **certain** you are wrong.
I am **sure** you are wrong.

➡ **Certain** also means **some**.
Certain birds cannot fly.
Some birds cannot fly.

chair

➡ A **chair** is something you sit on. A **chair** may be made of wood, metal, or plastic. A **chair** may be hard or soft to sit on.

chalk

➡ **Chalk** is a very soft stone. A stick of **chalk** is used to write on a blackboard. Most **chalk** is white.

change

➡ **Change** is the **money you get back when you buy** something.

Todd had **25¢**

He bought gum for **10¢**

Todd's **change** was **15¢**

➡ To **change** means to **become different**.
The weather **changed** from sunshine to rain.
The weather **became different**.

➡ To **change** also means to **make** something **different**.
Robin **changed** her shoes. Robin put on a **different** pair of shoes.

chase → To **chase** means to **run after.**
The cat **chased** the mouse.
The cat **ran after** the mouse.

cheek → Your **cheek** is part of your body. You have two **cheeks.** They are the parts of your face below your eyes and on either side of your nose and mouth.

cherry → A **cherry** is a small round fruit that is usually red. **Cherries** grow on trees. **Cherry** trees have pink flowers.

chew → To **chew** means to **break food into small pieces with your teeth.**

Carol **chewed** a piece of apple. Carol **used her teeth to make** the apple into **many small pieces.**

chicken → A **chicken** is a bird. A mother **chicken** is called a hen. Hens lay eggs. Did you have an **egg** for breakfast this morning? A father **chicken** is called a rooster. A young **chicken** is called a chick.
People eat the meat of **chickens.**

child → A **child** is a **young person.** A **girl** is a **child.** A **boy** is also a **child.** David is a **boy.** Mary is a **girl.** Mary and David are **children.**

chin ⇨ Your **chin** is a part of your body. It is the part of your face just below your mouth.

---

chocolate ⇨ **Chocolate** is a flavor. The flavor comes from a brown bean that grows on a tree. **Chocolate** is used to make candy and cake and other sweet things we eat.

---

choose ⇨ To **choose** means to **pick out** one thing from many things.

The man said, "I have chocolate, vanilla, and strawberry ice cream. Which do you **choose?**" Ellen said, "I **choose** vanilla." Jackie **chose** chocolate. No one **chose** strawberry. Strawberry was not **chosen.**

---

circle ⇨ A **circle** is a round, flat shape. A ring is shaped like a **circle.** A penny is also shaped like a **circle.**

⇨ To **circle** means to **go around** something.

The dog's collar **circles** its neck.
The dog's collar **goes around** its neck.

⇨ To **circle** also means to **draw a line around** something.

Circle the right answer.
Draw a line around the right answer.

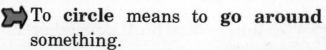

circus

A **circus** is a show that has many people and animals. The people and animals do tricks that make us happy. The clowns in the **circus** make us laugh.

Circuses travel from town to town. Have you ever been to a **circus?**

clean

city

A **city** is a large town. A **city** has many buildings. Many people live in **cities.**

clap

To **clap** means to **hit your hands together** to make a noise. We **clap** to show we like something.

class

A **class** is a **group of children in school** who learn things together. The room where the **class** sits is called a classroom.

clean

Clean means **not dirty.**

"Are your hands dirty?" asked Mother. "No," said Sam, "my hands are **not dirty.** My hands are **clean,** because I washed them.

climb To **climb** means to **use your hands and feet to go up** something. People **climb** ladders, trees, stairs, and other things.

---

clock A **clock** is a machine that **shows what time it is.** Many **clocks** have two hands. The hands point to numbers on the **clock.**

"What time is it?" asked Mother. Brian looked at the **clock** and said, "It is seven o'clock."

---

close Close means **near.**
My friend's house is **close** to mine.
My friend's house is **near** mine.

To **close** means to **shut** something.
Close the door when you leave.
Shut the door when you leave. Do not leave the door open.

To **be closed** means to **not be open.**
Philip's eyes are **closed.**
Philip's eyes are **not open.**

---

closet A **closet** is a very small room where clothes and other things are kept. Most **closets** have doors.

---

cloth Cloth is what most clothes are made from. Wool, silk, and cotton are some kinds of **cloth.**

clothes

Clothes are **what people wear.**
Hats, coats, shirts, pants, dresses, socks, and shoes are kinds of **clothes.**

cloud

A **cloud** is the white or gray shape you sometimes see in the sky. **Clouds** are made of tiny drops of water. Some **clouds** are white and puffy. Other **clouds** are big and dark. Rain always falls from **clouds.**

clown

A **clown** is a **person who tries to make us laugh.** A **clown** paints his or her face to look happy or sad. **Clowns** wear colorful clothes and do silly things.

coat

A **coat** is **something you wear** when it is cold. You wear a **coat** on top of all your other clothes to keep warm.

A **coat** is also an **animal's fur.** Cats, dogs, and bears have **coats.**

coin

A **coin** is a small, round piece of metal that is used as **money.** A cent is a **coin.** A nickel and a dime are also **coins.**

cold

➤ **Cold** means **not hot**. Ice is always **cold**.

➤ A **cold** is a kind of sickness. A **cold** makes you sneeze, blow your nose, and have a sore throat. Hugh has a bad **cold**. He is very sick.

---

color

➤ Red, yellow, and blue are **colors**. Orange, green, and purple are also **colors**. How many other **colors** can you name?

➤ To **color** means to **put color on** something. Crayons and paint are used to **color** things.
Are you going to **color** the picture?
Yes, I am going to **put yellow and red paint on** the picture.

comb

➤ A **comb** is used to make hair look neat.

➤ To **comb** means to **put a comb through hair.** Mother says, "Please **comb** your hair before you go to school." Mother wants your hair to look neat when you go to school.

---

come

➤ To **come** means to **move toward** someone. Chip said to his dog, "**Come**." The dog **came**. The dog **moved toward** Chip.

➤ To **come** means to **arrive** at a place. Grandpa will be **coming** at noon. Grandpa will be **arriving** at noon. Grandpa will be here at noon.

container ⟩ A **container** is used to hold things. **Containers** can be made of wood, metal, glass, plastic, paper, or other things. A bag and a basket are two kinds of **containers.** A shoe box is a **container** that holds shoes. When you buy soda, what kind of **container** does it come in?

cook ⟩ To **cook** means to **make food ready to eat** by heating it.
Mother is **cooking** soup.
She is **heating** it on top of the stove.

⟩ A **cook** is a **person who makes food ready to eat.**
Who is going to be the **cook** today? I am going to be the **cook** today. I am going to make breakfast.

cookie ⟩ A **cookie** is a sweet food that looks like a very small, thin cake. **Cookies** can be made in many kinds of shapes, colors, and flavors. **Cookies** are baked in an oven. Milk and **cookies** make a good snack.

cool ⟩ Cool means **not warm.**
It was **cool** under the trees.
It was **not warm** under the trees. It was warm under the sun, but it was **cool** in the shade of the trees.

43

copy

➤ To **copy** someone means to **act like** him or her. Steve put his hands on his head. Warren **copied** Steve. Warren also put his hands on his head.

➤ To **copy** something is to **make another one** that looks just like it.

Can you make a **copy** of this picture?
Can you **make another** picture that looks the same?
Can you **copy** this number?

3

---

corn

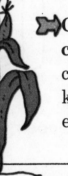

➤ Corn is a food that grows on a tall plant. The **corn** plant makes small pieces of yellow **corn**, called kernels or grains, that we eat. Many kernels of **corn** grow together on a cob. Have you ever eaten **corn** on the cob?

---

corner

➤ A **corner** is a **place where two flat things meet and make an edge.**
My dog likes to sleep in the **corner.**
My dog likes to sleep in the **place where** the **two walls meet.**

➤ A **corner** is an **edge** of something.
The **corner** of the table is sharp.
The **edge** of the table is sharp.

➤ A **corner** is also the place **where two streets come together.**
The mailbox stands on the **corner.**
The mailbox stands **where the two streets meet.**

cost

➤ **Cost** means **how much money you need** to buy something.

The **cost** of a new pen is 29¢. To buy a new pen, you need 29¢. A new pen **costs** 29¢.

---

could

➤ **Could** means **was able.**

Betsy **could** read when she was seven years old.

Betsy **was able** to read when she was seven years old.

---

count

➤ To **count** means to say **numbers in the right order.**

I can **count** up to ten. I can **say one, two, three, four, five, six, seven, eight, nine, ten.**

1 2 3 4 5 6 7 8 9 10

➤ To **count** also means to **find how many.**

When Nancy **counted** the cookies in the box, she **found** thirty-two cookies.

---

country

➤ The **country** is a place where there are many trees, plants, and animals, but not many people.

Matthew and his family live in the **country.** Sometimes they visit Matthew's grandparents, who live in the city.

45

cover ⇨ To **cover** means to **put one thing on top of another.**

Please **cover** your head. **Put on** a hat.

⇨ A **cover** is something that **goes over another thing.**

My book has a **cover** that keeps it clean.

---

cow ⇨ A **cow** is a large animal. **Cows** give us the milk and cream we drink. Cheese and butter are made from **cow's** milk. A farm that has many **cows** is called a dairy farm. A young **cow** is called a calf.

---

cracker ⇨ A **cracker** is a food. It is small and thin. **Crackers** are dry and sometimes salty.

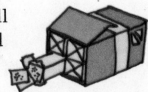

---

crayon ⇨ A **crayon** is a **stick of colored wax.** A **crayon** is used to put color on paper.

---

cross ⇨ A **cross** is a shape that is made when **one line goes over, or across, another line.**

The sign + is a **cross.** The letter **X** is also a **cross.** The red **cross** on a first-aid kit means that there are things inside to make hurt or sick people feel better.

crowd

➡ A **crowd** is **many people** in one place.
A **crowd** watched the football game.
A **big group of people** watched the game.

cry

➡ To **cry** means to **have drops of water** called tears **come out of your eyes**. People **cry** when they are very sad or hurt.

➡ A **cry** is a **shout**.
"I win!" **cried** Michelle.
"I win!" **shouted** Michelle
"I win!" **yelled** Michelle.

➡ A **cry** is also the **sound an animal makes**.
A cow **cries** "moo." An owl **cries** "hoot."

cup

➡ A **cup** is a kind of container you drink from. Most **cups** have handles.
People drink tea, coffee, and cocoa from **cups**.

cut

➡ To **cut** means to **use scissors or a knife to make something into smaller pieces**.
I **cut** the sandwich in half. I **used a knife to make two smaller pieces**.

I use scissors to **cut** paper into many smaller shapes.

➡ A **cut** is a **hurt, bleeding place on your skin**.
I have a **cut** on my knee. The **cut** is **where I was hurt** when I fell down.

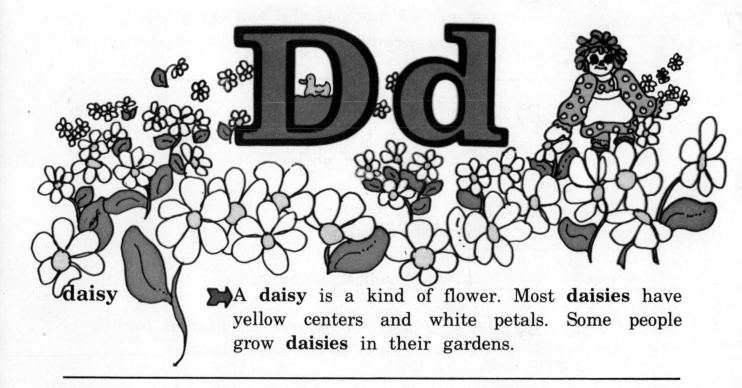

Dd

daisy

➤ A **daisy** is a kind of flower. Most **daisies** have yellow centers and white petals. Some people grow **daisies** in their gardens.

dance

➤ To **dance** means to **move your body in time to music.**

Albert likes to **dance.** When Albert hears music, he likes to **jump and turn, moving along with the music.** Albert likes **dancing.** He is a good dancer.

➤ A **dance** is a **party where people dance.**
Mom and Dad are going to a **dance** tonight.

➤ A **dancer** is **someone who dances.**
A ballet **dancer** wears special shoes.

danger

➤ **Danger** is **something that can hurt** you.
When you play with matches, you are in **danger.**
When you play with matches, you **might get hurt.**

dark

→ **Dark** means **not light.**
We play outside until it is **dark.**
We play outside until there is **no light.**

This is **dark** blue. This is **light** blue.

→ The **dark** is the **time when there is no light.**
We came home in the **dark.**
We came home in the **night.**

→ The **dark** is a **place where there is no light.**
We hid in the **dark** of the room.
We hid in the part of the room **where there was no light.**

daughter

→ A **daughter** is the **girl child** of her mother and father. A woman is the **daughter** of her mother and father also.
Vera is a girl. Vera is the **daughter** of her mother and father. Vera's mother is the **daughter** of Vera's grandparents.

day

→ A **day** is the **night and the day together.**
A **day** is twenty-four hours long. There are seven **days** in a week. The **days** of the week are Sunday, Monday, Tuesday, Wednesday, Thursday, Friday, and Saturday.

49

deep

deep

⇨ **Deep** means a **long way down.**
The treasure was buried **deep** in the ground. You have to dig **far into** the ground to find the buried treasure.

⇨ **Deep** also means **how far down** something goes. How **deep** is the lake? The lake is twenty feet **deep.**

deer

⇨ A **deer** is an animal that has four long thin legs. **Deer** run very fast. A mother **deer** is called a doe. A father **deer** is called a buck or stag. A young **deer** is called a fawn.

dentist

⇨ A **dentist** is a kind of doctor. A **dentist** knows all about teeth. **Dentists** help you to keep your teeth healthy.

desk

⇨ A **desk** is a kind of table. You sit at a **desk** to write letters and to do your homework A classroom has many **desks.**

dessert

⇨ **Dessert** is something sweet that you eat after lunch or dinner. Cake, pudding, fruit, and ice cream are **desserts.**

dictionary

⇨ A **dictionary** is a **book that tells what words mean.** The book you are looking at now is a **dictionary.**

different ➡ **Different** means **not the same.**
My name is Barbara. Your name is Larry.
Our names are **different.**
Our names are **not the same.**

---

difficult ➡ **Difficult** means **hard to do.**
You have asked me a **difficult** question.
You have asked me a **hard** question. It is **not easy** to answer your question.

---

dime ➡ A **dime** is a piece of money. It is made of metal.
A **dime** is the same as **ten cents.** It is also written as **10¢.** Ten **dimes** make one dollar.

---

dinner ➡ **Dinner** is the **biggest meal** of the day. Some people eat **dinner** in the middle of the day. Other people eat **dinner** later, in the evening.

---

direction ➡ A **direction** tells **how to do** something.
Before we played the game, we read the **directions.** We read the **directions** to learn **how to play** the game.

➡ A **direction** is **where something goes to.**
The ball rolled in the **direction** of the tree.
The ball rolled **toward** the tree.

➡ A **direction** is also **where something comes from.**
What **direction** did the noise **come from?**
I don't know **where** the noise **came from.**

dirt

dirt

➡️ **Dirt** is the same as **earth** or **soil**. **Dirt** is what trees, grass, and flowers grow in.

---

dirty

➡️ **Dirty** means **not neat and clean.**
The kitchen is **dirty.**
The kitchen is **messy.**
The kitchen is **not neat and clean.**

---

discover

➡️ To **discover** means to **find** something.
Diane **discovered** a cave. Diane was the first person to **find** the cave. No one had ever been in the cave.

---

dish

➡️ A **dish** is **something to put food on.**
You eat food from a **dish.** Plates, bowls, cups, and saucers are **dishes.**

➡️ A **dish** is also any kind of **cooked food.**
Spaghetti is my favorite **dish.** I love to eat a **dish** of spaghetti.

---

distance

➡️ **Distance** means how **far** something is.
It is a long **distance** to the store. The store is very **far.** The store is **not close.**

What is the **distance** between the two trees? How **far** is it between the two trees?

52

do

Do you know how to swim? Yes, I **do** know how to swim. My sister **does** also.

What are you **doing?** I am reading a book.

Did you buy milk and bread at the store? Yes, I **did** buy milk and bread.

---

doctor

A **doctor** is a person who knows how to make you better when you are sick. **Doctors** also know how to help you keep from getting sick.

---

dog

A **dog** is a furry animal with four legs. There are many kinds of **dogs.** Some **dogs** are taught to help people do work. **Dogs** also make good pets. Do you know someone who has a pet **dog?** A young **dog** is called a puppy.

---

doll

A **doll** is a toy that is made to look like a person. Do you have a favorite **doll?** Does your **doll** have a name? This **doll** is made of cloth. She is fun to play with.

---

dollar

A **dollar** is an amount of money. A **dollar** is the same as **one hundred cents.** A **dollar** bill is a piece of paper money that is the same as **one hundred cents** The sign $ means **dollars.**

$1.00 = one dollar = one hundred cents
$5.00 = five dollars = five hundred cents

53

dolphin

dolphin ➡A **dolphin** is a kind of animal that swims. **Dolphins** live in the sea, but they are not fish. They are friendly animals. **Dolphins** are also smart. They can be taught to do tricks.

---

door ➡A **door** is a large, flat piece of wood, metal, or glass. A **door** is used to keep something closed. To get into a house or an apartment, you open the front **door.** A refrigerator has a **door** to keep the cold inside. Can you think of other things that have **doors?**

---

double ➡**Double** means **two** times as much of a thing.
I took a **double** helping of pie.
I took **two** helpings of pie.

Six is the **double** of three.
Six is **two** times as much as three.
Six is **twice** as much as three.

---

down ➡**Down** means the **opposite of up.**
Carl walked **down** the stairs.
Carl walked **from the top** of the stairs **to the bottom** of the stairs.

I fell **down** and hurt my knee.
I fell **to the ground** and hurt my knee.

---

dozen ➡ A **dozen** is **twelve** of a thing.
Mother sent me to the store to buy a **dozen** eggs. I bought **twelve** eggs in a carton.

54

dragon

A **dragon** is a kind of make-believe animal that lives only in stories. **Dragons** are big and have sharp claws and teeth. Some **dragons** have wings. Some **dragons** breathe fire. In many stories, **dragons** are mean. There are also stories about friendly **dragons.**

draw

To **draw** means to **make a picture** of something with a crayon or a pencil.
I like to **draw.**
I like to **make pictures.** I am **drawing** a picture of a house. Yesterday, I **drew** a car.

dress

To **dress** means to **put on clothes.**
I took a bath before I **dressed.**
I took a bath before I **put on my clothes.**

A **dress** is a kind of clothes. A **dress** is a skirt and a top in one piece.
Sally put on a clean **dress** for the party.

drill

A **drill** is a tool that is used to make holes in wood, metal, and other things.

To **drill** means to **use a drill** to make holes.
I am **drilling** a piece of wood.
I am **using a drill** to make a hole in a piece of wood.

drink

drink

➦ To **drink** means to **eat** something **liquid.**
I like to **drink** milk. How many glasses of milk have I **drunk** today? I **drank** four glasses of milk today.

➦ A **drink** is something **liquid you eat.**
When I am very thirsty, I like a **drink** of orange juice.

---

drive

➦ To **drive** means to **make a car** or a bus or a truck **move.**
Someday I will learn to **drive.** I will learn how to **make a car move.**

➦ To **drive** means to use a car to go someplace.
We are **driving** to Grandma's house.
We are **using the car to go** to Grandma's.

---

drop

➦ To **drop** means to **fall,** or to **make something fall.**
The leaves are **dropping** from the tree.
The leaves are **falling** from the tree.

I **dropped** my spoon on the floor. The spoon **fell** to the floor.

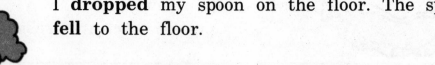

➦ A **drop** is a **little bit of a liquid.**
There is only a **drop** of milk left.
There is only a **little bit** of milk left. **Not much** milk is left.

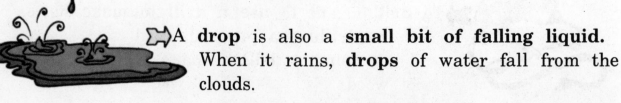

➦ A **drop** is also a **small bit of falling liquid.**
When it rains, **drops** of water fall from the clouds.

56

drum

A **drum** is a kind of musical instrument. You hit or beat a **drum** to make music.
I play a **drum** in the school band.

To **drum** means to **beat a drum.**
We heard him **drumming** all day.
We heard him **beating the drum** all day.

---

dry

Dry means **not wet.**
The summer has been **dry.** It has **not** been a **wet** summer. It has not rained all summer.

The juice bottle is **dry.** There is no more juice in the bottle.

To **dry** means to **take away wetness.**
I **dried** my hands with a towel. I wiped the water from my hands with a towel.

To **dry** means to **let something become dry.**
We waited for the paint to **dry.** We waited for the wet paint to **not be wet.**

---

duck

A **duck** is a kind of bird that can swim. **Ducks** have pieces of skin between their toes called webs. The webs help **ducks** to swim. When a **duck** makes a sound, it goes, "quack."

---

during

During means **at the same time.**
During dinner, we listened to music.
We ate dinner and listened to music **at the same time.**
While we ate dinner, we listened to music.
As we ate dinner, we listened to music.

18 Ee

each

→ **Each** means **every one** of something.

Each flower is a different color.

Every one of the flowers is a different color.

eagle

→ An **eagle** is a kind of bird that is very large. **Eagles** are good hunters. A quarter has a picture of an **eagle** on it.

ear

→ An **ear** is the part of your body that you hear with. You have two **ears,** one on **each** side of your head.

early

→ **Early** means in the **first part** of something.

I eat breakfast **early** in the day.

I eat breakfast in the **beginning** of the day.

→ **Early** also means something happening **sooner than usual.**

Wilson is ill. He will go to bed **early.** Wilson will go to bed **sooner than** he **usually** does.

earth

Earth is what plants grow in. Some animals and insects make their homes in **earth. Earth** is also called **soil.** It is also called **ground.**

The **earth** is our **world.** All people, animals, and plants live on the **earth.**

---

easy

Easy means **not hard** to do.
Roller-skating is **easy** to do.
Roller-skating is **not hard** to do. It is **simple** to roller-skate.

---

eat

To **eat** means to **put food in your mouth, chew it, and swallow it.**
I love to **eat** bananas. I am **eating** a banana now. Yesterday, I **ate** two bananas. Soon I will have **eaten** all my bananas.

---

egg

An **egg** is a kind of food. The **eggs** we eat come from chickens. Outside, **eggs** have a hard part called a shell. Inside, **eggs** have two soft parts. One part, called the white, is clear, but turns white when cooked. The other part is called the yolk. The yolk is always yellow.

All birds lay **eggs.** Baby birds grow in **eggs.**

---

eight

Eight is a number. **Eight** is also written as **8.** Can you count the number of marbles?

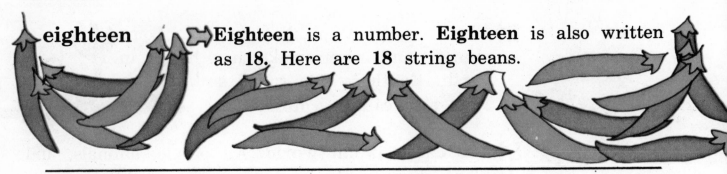

eighteen

Eighteen is a number. **Eighteen** is also written as **18.** Here are **18** string beans.

eighty

Eighty is a number. It is also written as **80.** Eight dimes make **eighty** cents.

either

Either means **one or the other.**
I don't want **either** milk or juice.
I don't want **one or the other.** I don't want milk. I don't want juice.

Either also means **each one of two** things.
Clara held a cookie in **either** hand.
Clara held a cookie in **each** hand.

elbow

Your **elbow** is a part of your body. It is the part of your arm that bends.

elephant

An **elephant** is the biggest animal in the world. **Elephants** have big ears and long noses called trunks. They also have two long teeth called tusks. Have you ever seen an **elephant?**

eleven  ➤ **Eleven** is a number. It is also written as **11.** Here are **eleven** pencils.

---

empty ➤ **Empty** means having **nothing inside.** The cookie jar is **empty.** There is **nothing inside** the cookie jar.

➤ To **empty** means to **take everything out** of something.
I **emptied** my toy chest.
I **took** all the toys out of my toy chest.

---

end ➤ An **end** is **where something begins or stops.**
A pencil has two **ends.** One **end** has a point.
The other **end** has an eraser.

➤ The **end** is the **last part** of something.
Who ate the **end** of the bread?
Who ate the **last piece** of the bread?

➤ To **end** means to **stop.**
The rain **ended,** and the sun came out.
The rain **stopped,** and the sun came out.

---

engine ➤ An **engine** is a **machine that makes something work.** Cars and airplanes have **engines.** An **engine** is also called a **motor.**

---

enjoy ➤ To **enjoy** means to **have fun** doing something.
We **enjoyed** swimming at the beach.
We **had fun** swimming at the beach.

enough   ➡ Enough means as much **as you need or want** of a thing.
I have **enough** sugar to make a cake.
I have **as much** sugar **as I need.**

---

enter   ➡ To **enter** means to **go into** something.
We **entered** the movie at two o'clock.
We **went into** the movie at two o'clock

---

entire   ➡ **Entire** means **all** of something.
Scott ate the **entire** candy bar.
Scott ate the **whole** candy bar. He ate **all** of it.

➡ It snowed the **entire** day.
It snowed **all** day.

---

equal   ➡ **Equal** means the **same.**
Each person had an **equal** amount of money.
Each person had the **same** amount of money.

➡ To **equal** means to **be the same.**
One dozen **equals** twelve.
One dozen **is the same** as twelve.

The sign = means **is equal to.**
Three and four **are equal to** seven.

3+4=7

even   ⮞Even means **smooth and unbroken.**
The floor is **even.**
The floor is **smooth and unbroken.**

⮞Even also means that **two or more things are the same in some way.**
The piles of books are **even.** They **are the same** in height.

---

ever   ⮞Ever means **at any time.**
Have you **ever** been in an airplane?
Have you **at any time** been in an airplane?

---

every   ⮞Every means **each one** of something.
Every child ate a cupcake.
Each child ate a cupcake.

⮞Every also means **all.**
Every crayon I have is broken.
All my crayons are broken.

---

extra   ⮞Extra means **more than.**
Ernie has an **extra** piece of gum.
Ernie has **more** gum **than** he wants.

I got an **extra** present.
I got one **more** present **than** I expected.

---

eye   ⮞An **eye** is the part of your body that you see with. You have two **eyes** on your face, one above each cheek. Are your **eyes** blue, brown, or green?

Ff

face   ⇨ Your **face** is a part of your body. Your eyes, nose, and mouth are parts of your **face.**

---

fall   ⇨ To **fall** means to **drop to the ground.**
When I **fall,** I sometimes hurt myself. Yesterday, I **fell** from my bicycle. I had never **fallen** from my bicycle before. I do not like **falling.**

⇨ The **fall** is one of the four seasons of the year. It is the time between the warm summer and the cold winter. In the **fall,** the leaves of some trees turn to yellow, red, orange, and brown, and fall from the trees. **Fall** is also called **autumn.**

family   ⇨ Roger lives with his **family.** Roger lives with his mother, his father, his sister, and his brother. Roger's grandparents, aunts, uncles, and cousins are also his **family,** but he does not live with them.

far

➡ **Far** means **not near.**
Becky lives **far** from her school. Her home is **not near** her school.

➡ **Far** also means **distance.**
How **far** did Pam's bunny jump?
What **distance** did it jump? It jumped **far.** Nick's bunny jumped **farther.** It jumped a bigger distance. My bunny jumped **farthest.** It jumped the biggest distance.

---

farm

➡ A **farm** is a **place where food is grown.** On a **farm,** you might see a vegetable garden and fruit trees. You might see cows, pigs, chickens, and horses. People who live on a **farm** and help things to grow are called farmers.

fast

➡ **Fast** means **quick.**
Anita is a **fast** runner.
Anita is a **quick** runner. When she runs, she is **not slow.**

I can hop **fast.**
I can walk **faster.**
I can run **fastest.**

---

father

➡ A **father** is a man who has a child. A **father** is sometimes called **Dad, Daddy,** or **Pop.** Marion and Doug are their **father's** children.

favorite

favorite ➡ **Favorite** means **liked the most.**
What is your **favorite** color? What color do you **like the most?**

---

fear ➡ To **fear** something means to **be afraid** of it.
Ramona does not **fear** thunder.
Ramona is not **afraid** of thunder. She knows it cannot hurt her.

---

feel ➡ To **feel** means to **touch** something.
I like to **feel** my hamster's fur.
I like to **touch** my hamster's fur.

➡ To **feel** also means **how you are.**
Yesterday, Gwenn **felt** sick. She **was** sick yesterday, but today she **feels** better.

---

fence ➡ A **fence** is a kind of wall. A playground **fence** keeps children and playthings inside. A garden **fence** keeps animals outside.

---

few ➡ **Few** means a **small number** of something.
I have a **few** pennies.
I have a **small number** of pennies.
I have **not many** pennies.

---

field ➡ A **field** is a large, flat piece of land that has no trees or buildings. Food is grown on a farm's **fields.** Baseball is played on a baseball **field.**

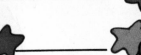fire

fifteen ➡️ **Fifteen** is a number. It is also written as **15.** Here are **fifteen** stars.

fifty ➡️ **Fifty** is a number. **Fifty** is also written as **50.** Ten nickels are **fifty** cents.

fill ➡️ To **fill** means to **take up all the room.**
I **filled** my glass with juice.
I **took up all the room** in my glass. The glass is **full. No more** juice **fits** into it.

find ➡️ To **find** means to **come upon** something.
I was lucky to **find** a nickel.
I was lucky to **come upon** a nickel. I'm glad I **found** a nickel.

➡️ To **find** also means to **have a thought** about something.
I **found** the story to be sad.
I **thought** it was a sad story.

finger ➡️ A **finger** is a part of your body. You have five **fingers** at the end of each hand.

fire ➡️ **Fire** is very hot and bright. **Fire** is good when it is used to cook food and to keep us warm. **Fire** is bad when it burns, or hurts, people and things. Never play with **fire.**

fire fighter ➡️ A **fire fighter** is a **person who puts out fires.**
Fire fighters wear special clothes to keep them
from getting burned.

fire truck ➡️ To go to a fire, fire fighters ride in a **fire truck.**
Fire trucks carry water, hoses, ladders, and
other things fire fighters need to fight fires. A
fire truck is also called a **fire engine.**

first ➡️ **First** means to **come before** other things.
One is the **first** number.
One **comes before** all other numbers.

' This is my **first** bicycle. I have never had a
bicycle before.

When I eat lunch, I **first** wash my hands.
I wash my hands **before** I eat lunch.

fish ➡️ A **fish** is an animal that lives in water. **Fish**
have fins to help them swim. Some **fish** live in
lakes and rivers. Other **fish** live in the sea. Do
you like to eat **fish?**

➡️ To **fish** means to **try to catch fish.**
Marty is **fishing.**
Marty is **trying to catch fish.**

fit

To **fit** means to be the **right size**.
Nora's coat **fits.** Her coat is **not too big or too small.** It is the **right size.**

All the berries do not **fit** in the basket. The basket is too small. There are too many berries to **fit** into the basket.

---

five

Five is a number. It is also written as **5.** Here are **five** flowers.

---

fix

To **fix** means to **put together** something that is broken or not working.
Can Humpty Dumpty be **fixed?**
Can Humpty Dumpty be **put together** again?

---

flat

Flat means **smooth and even.**
The floor is **flat.**
The floor is **smooth and even.** It has **no low spots or high spots.**

Flat also means **spread out.**
Emil is lying **flat** on the bed.
Emil is **spread out** on the bed.

A **flat** is a **tire that has lost its air.**
My bike has a **flat.** There is **no air in the tire.**

float

To **float** means to **stay on top of a liquid.**
My toy boat **floats.**
My toy boat **stays on top of the water.** It does **not sink.**

To **float** also means to **be carried by air.**
A feather **floats** in air.
A feather **can be carried by the air** from place to place. It **does not fall** to the ground.

---

floor

The **floor** is the flat **bottom part of a room.**
We walk on the **floor.**

A **floor** is also a part of a building. A **floor** is sometimes called a **storey.**
Irene's house has two **floors,** or **storeys.** The first **floor** has a dining room, a living room, and a kitchen. The bedrooms and bathrooms are on the second **floor.**

---

flour

Flour is tiny bits of wheat, corn, or other grains. **Flour** is used to make bread, cake, cookies, and other foods.

---

flower

A **flower** is the part of a plant that makes seeds. **Flowers** are also called **blossoms. Flowers** come in beautiful colors. Many **flowers** also have a good smell. Daffodils, pansies, and daisies are **flowers.** Some people grow **flowers** in their gardens.

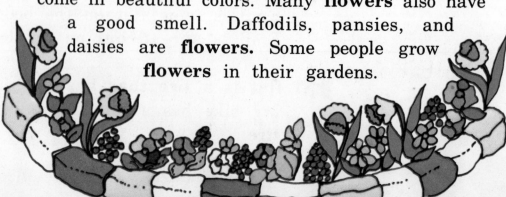

fly

To **fly** means to **move through the air.**
Birds **fly.**
Birds **move through the air.** Airplanes **fly** also. When you throw a ball, it **flies** through the air.

A **fly** is a kind of bug or insect. It is very small. **Flies** have two wings that you can see through.

---

follow

To **follow** means to **come after or behind.**
The afternoon **follows** the morning.
The afternoon **comes after** the morning.

---

food

Food is **what we eat** to make us grow and keep our bodies healthy. Milk is a **food.** Meat, fruit and vegetables are also **foods.**

---

foot

Your **foot** is a part of your body. You have two **feet,** one at the end of each leg. People walk on their **feet.**

Some animals also have **feet.** A squirrel is an animal with four **feet.**

---

football

Football is a game. Two teams play **football** on a big field of grass. The team that carries, kicks, or throws the ball to its end of the field the most times wins.

for

➡ I used a crayon **for** a pencil.
I used a crayon **in place of** a pencil.

➡ Stan went to the library **for** me. Stan went to the library. I did not have to go.

➡ Ralph has left **for** school.
Ralph has left **to go to** school.

➡ Mary Beth delivers newspapers **for** money.
Mary Beth delivers newspapers **to get** money.

➡ What are you looking **for?** We are looking **for** seashells. We are **trying to find** them.

➡ Duane has money **for** lunch.
Duane has money **to buy** lunch.

forest

➡ A **forest** is a **large group of trees and other plants.** Many animals live in **forests.** Deer and owls make their homes in the **forest.** A **forest** is also called a **wood.**

forget

➡ **Forget** means to **not remember.**
Did you **forget** to bring the present?
I did **not remember** to bring it.
I **forgot.**

fork

➡ A **fork** is a tool used for eating. At one end, **forks** have sharp points that can hold food. **Forks** make it easy for us to lift food to our mouths.

forty

→ **Forty** is a number. It is also written as **40**. Four dimes are **forty** cents.

forward

→ The **forward** part of something is its **front**.
The motor is in the **forward** part of the car.
The motor is in the **front** part of the car.

→ **Forward** also means going to a place in front.
Debbie ran **forward**.
Debbie ran **ahead**.
Debbie ran **to a place in front**.

four

→ **Four** is a number. It is also written as **4**. Here are **four** cupcakes.

fourteen

→ **Fourteen** is a number. It is also written as **14**. Can you count the **fourteen** ladybugs?

friend

→ Your **friend** is someone you know and like. Your **friend** also likes you. It is fun to play with your **friends**.

frog

→ A **frog** is a small animal with four strong legs. **Frogs** are good jumpers. Some **frogs** live on land. Other **frogs** live in water.

from

from

    ➤We walked home **from** school. We left school and walked to our home.

    ➤I played **from** two until four o'clock.
I played **between** two and four o'clock.

    ➤Sheila took a candy **from** the jar.
Sheila took a candy **out of** the jar.

    ➤I got a toy **from** Bud. He gave a toy to me.

    ➤Three **from** five is two. The **difference between** three and five is two.

---

front

    ➤The **front** of something is opposite, or at the other end of, its back.
        An arrow has a point in **front.** The feathers are at the back.

    ➤To **come in front** means to **come before.**
The letter A **comes in front of** B.
The letter A **comes before** B.

    ➤To **be in front** means to **be before** something.
The teacher stands **in front of** the class.
The teacher stands **before** the class.

---

fruit

    ➤**Fruit** is a food that grows on trees, bushes, and vines. Plums and lemons are **fruits** that grow on trees. Raspberries are a **fruit** that grows on bushes. Watermelons and grapes are **fruits** that grow on vines.

full

➤ **Full** means having **no more room inside.**
The bucket is **full** of water.
The bucket has **no more room** for water. **No more** water **will fit** in the bucket.

I am **full.** There is **no more room** in my stomach for food.

➤ **Full** also means having **many things inside.**
A library is **full** of books. There are a great **many** books in a library.

---

fun

➤ **Fun** is anything that **makes us happy.**
Going to the circus is **fun.** We always **have a good time.**

---

funny

➤ **Funny** means **able to make us laugh.**
Grandpa tells stories that are **funny.**
Grandpa tells stories that **make us laugh.**

---

fur

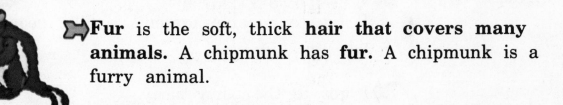

➤ **Fur** is the soft, thick **hair that covers many animals.** A chipmunk has **fur.** A chipmunk is a furry animal.

---

furniture

➤ **Furniture** is tables, chairs, desks, and beds. A bookcase and a sofa are also kinds of **furniture.**

game A **game** is something that is **fun to play**. Hide-and-seek and baseball are **games**.

garden A **garden** is a **place where people grow plants.** Roses and daisies and tulips are grown in flower **gardens.** Peas and pumpkins and cabbage are grown in vegetable **gardens.**

get I like to **get** presents.
I like to **receive** presents. I like people to give me presents.

I **got** to the party early.
I **reached** the party early. I **arrived** early.

Please **get** some milk.
Please **go** to the store **and buy** some milk.

Add one and two to **get** three.
Add one and two to **make** three.

It is **getting** dark outside.
It is **becoming** dark outside.

giant   ➡ **Giant** means **very big,** or **huge.**
An elephant is a **giant** animal.
An elephant is **very big.** It is **huge.**

➡ A **giant** is a make-believe person who is very tall and strong. **Giants** live only in stories. Do you know a story about a **giant?**

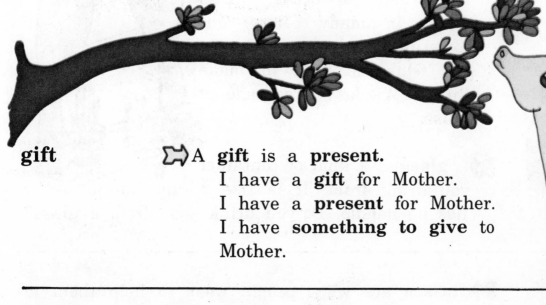

gift   ➡ A **gift** is a **present.**
I have a **gift** for Mother.
I have a **present** for Mother.
I have **something to give** to Mother.

giraffe   ➡ A **giraffe** is the tallest animal in the world. **Giraffes** have four long legs and a very long neck.

girl   ➡ A **girl** is a **young person.** Sandra is a **girl.** When she grows up she will be a woman. Sandra's mother is a woman.

give   ➡ Dennis wants to **give** his sister a book. Dennis is **giving** his sister a book. He has **given** the book to his sister. She has the book. Now she is reading it.

glad

➤ **Glad** means **happy.**
Elaine is **glad** when it snows.
Elaine is **happy** when it snows.

---

glass

➤ **Glass** is something hard that you can usually see through. It is easy to break. **Glass** comes in many colors, but sometimes it has no color at all. **Glass** is used to make things. Windows are made of **glass.**

➤ A **glass** is a kind of container you drink from. It is like a cup, but it has no handle. Do you drink soda from a **glass?**

---

glasses

➤ **Glasses** are what people wear to help them to see better. Some **glasses** are made of glass.

---

glove

➤ A **glove** is a warm covering for your hand. **Gloves** are made to look like a person's hands. A **glove** has five fingers, one to cover each finger on a person's hand.

---

glue

➤ **Glue** is a thick liquid used to make things stick together.

➤ To **glue** means to **make things stick together.**
Dominick **glued** his broken toy.
Dominick **made the parts** of his toy **stick together.**

go

➡ A race car **goes** fast.
A race car **moves** fast.

➡ Is the clock **going?**
Is the clock **working?** Is it **running?**

➡ A sheep **goes** "baa."
A sheep **makes the sound** "baa."

➡ Annette's cold is **gone.** It **went** away. She doesn't have the cold any longer.

➡ The books **go** on the shelf.
The books **have a place** on the shelf.
The books **belong** on the shelf.

---

goat

➡ A **goat** is an animal that has long straight hair and two horns on its head. **Goats** have beards on their chins. A young **goat** is called a kid.

good

➡ Fruit is **good** for you to eat.
Eating fruit helps you to be healthy.

➡ Ice cream tastes **good.** I **like** the taste.

➡ Georgia is **good** to her pet.
Georgia is **kind** to her pet.

➡ When I go visiting, I wear my **good** shoes.
When I go visiting, I wear my **best** shoes.

good-by ➤Good-by is what you say when you leave someone. **Good-by** is also spelled **good-bye.**
When Joey left, he said, "**Good-by,** Mom."

good morning ➤Good morning is what you say to someone when you get up in the morning.
Wanda came to breakfast and said "**good morning**" to everyone.

good night ➤Good night is what you say when you go to sleep.
"**Good night,** Dad," said Jody, "I'm going to bed."

goose ➤A **goose** is a bird with a long neck. **Geese** can swim and fly. A father **goose** is called a gander. A young **goose** is called a gosling.

grandfather ➤A **grandfather** is a man whose son or daughter has a child.
Lydia calls her mother's father **Grandpa.**
Lydia calls her father's father **Granddad.**

grandmother ➤A **grandmother** is a woman whose daughter or son has a child.
Lionel calls his father's mother **Grandma.**
Lionel calls his mother's mother **Granny.**

grape

A **grape** is a small fruit that grows on a vine. **Grapes** may be purple, blue, red, or green. When you let a **grape** dry in the sun, you get a raisin.

---

grapefruit

A **grapefruit** is a large, round, yellow fruit that grows on a tree. **Grapefruit** juice is good to drink.

---

grass

Grass is a plant with long, thin, green leaves called blades. Sheep and cows are animals that eat **grass**. A lawn is the **grass** that people grow around their homes.

grasshopper

A **grasshopper** is a kind of bug or insect that has wings. **Grasshoppers** have strong back legs that make them good jumpers.

---

gray

Gray is a color. This is **gray**. Rain clouds are **gray**.

---

great

Great means **very big**.
An ostrich is a **great** bird.
An ostrich is a **very big** bird.

Great means being **very good at** something.
Horses are **great** runners.
Horses are **very good at** running.

81

green ⇒ **Green** is a color. This is **green**.
Most plants are **green**.

---

ground ⇒ The **ground** is what people walk on and plants grow in. Animals walk and crawl on top of the **ground**. Some animals make their homes in the **ground**. **Ground** is also called **earth**.

---

group ⇒ A **group** is **more than one** person or thing in the same place.
A **group** of children waited for the bus.
More than one child waited for the bus.

grow ⇒ To **grow** means to **get bigger**.
Dolores **grows** fast.
Dolores **gets bigger** fast. Last year, she **grew** four inches taller. She will be a big person when she is **grown**.

---

guest ⇒ A **guest** is a **person who comes to see you**.
Willy likes to have **guests**.
Willy likes to have **people come to see him**.
He likes to have **visitors**.

Hh

hair

➦**Hair** is a part of your body. Most of your **hair** grows on top of your head. Is the **hair** on your head curly or straight? Is it black, red, brown, or yellow?

Many animals have **hair** all over their bodies. An animal's **hair** is called fur.

---

half

➦A **half** is **one of two parts** of something. Each **half** is **the same size** as the other.
Beth has **half** an egg.
Beth has **one of two parts** of the egg.
Her part is **the same size** as the other part.

I have ten candies. I will give you **half.** We will each have five candies. We will each have **half** the candies.

➦To **halve** means to **make** something **into two parts of the same size.** We **halved** the sandwich. We **made** the sandwich into **two parts of the same size.**

83

hammer

hammer

➡️ A **hammer** is a tool used to hit nails to make them go into wood and other things. A **hammer** has a heavy metal part, called the head, that hits the nails. The **hammer's** other part, called the handle, is usually made of wood.

➡️ To **hammer** means to **use a hammer** to hit nails to make them go into wood and other things.
   Hammering is noisy.
   Using a hammer to hit nails to make them go into wood is noisy.

hand

➡️ Your **hand** is a part of your body. You have two **hands,** one at the end of each arm. At the end of each **hand,** you have five fingers.

handle

➡️ A **handle** makes it easy to hold something. The **handle** on a door makes opening and closing the door easy. The **handle** on a bag makes carrying the bag easy. Can you name some other things that have **handles?**

happen

➡️ When we heard the crash, we wondered what had **happened.**
When we heard the crash, we wondered what had **taken place.**

➡️ I **happened** to meet my friend. I didn't know I was going to meet my friend.

84

happy

▶ **Happy** means **feeling very pleased.**
Colleen is **happy.**
Colleen is **feeling very pleased.** She is **happy** because she won a prize in school.

---

hard

▶ **Hard** means **not soft.**
A rock is **hard.** You cannot change its shape because it is **not soft.** Clay is soft. You can push it into many different shapes.

▶ **Hard** also means **not easy** to do.
Sleeping is **hard** when you're not tired.
Sleeping **isn't easy** when you're not tired.

▶ **Hard** also means **strong.**
The wind was blowing **hard.**
The wind was blowing **strongly.**

---

hat

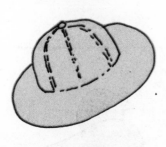

▶ A **hat** is a **covering for your head.** Some **hats** keep your head warm. Other **hats** keep your head from getting hurt. **Hats** are also used to keep the sun and rain out of your eyes. Your **hat** can show people what kind of job you do.

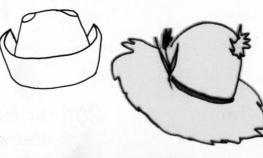

have

have

➡ To **have** something means it is yours.
We **have** a farm. We **own** a farm. The farm is **ours.** We **have** always **had** a farm.

Lucy **has** red hair. Her hair is red. I **have** red hair also. We **have** red hair.

➡ To **have to do** something means that you **must do** it.
I **have** to feed my cat before going out.
I **must** feed my cat before going out.

---

he

➡ Arnold is a boy
He is a boy. Who is Arnold?
　　　He is my older brother.

---

head

➡ Your **head** is the top part of your body. Your ears are part of your **head.**

---

health

➡ **Health** means **how good or bad a person's body feels.** If you are sick, you are in bad **health,** or unhealthy. If you are feeling good, you are in good **health,** or healthy.

---

hear

➡ To **hear** means to **use your ears to know sounds.**
I **heard** the birds chirping.
I **listened** to the birds chirping. I **used my ears to know the sound** they made.

Chirp Chirp Chirp

86

heart  Your **heart** is a part of your body.
Your **heart** is inside your chest.
Your **heart** keeps the blood moving
through your body.

 A **heart** is also a kind of shape.

heat Heat keeps us warm. The sun makes **heat.** A
fire also makes **heat.** When there is no **heat,** we
feel cold.

To **heat** means to **make something warm.**
Rodney **heated** soup for lunch.
Rodney **made** the soup **warm.**

heavy Heavy means **having much weight.**
A car is **heavy.**
A car **has much weight.** A car is too **heavy**
for a person to lift.

help To **help** means to **work with a person to make
something easier** to do.
Carlos and Juanita wanted to **help** their
friends to make a garden. They wanted to
make the work easier to do. They **helped**
their friends all day. They liked **helping**
them. Their friends thanked them for being so
helpful.

her Doreen's mother bought Doreen a new dress.
Her mother bought **her** a new dress.

here ▷ **Here** means **in this place.**
My comb is lost. Is it **here?**
Is my lost comb **in this place?**

---

hers ▷ The jump rope is Stacy's.
The jump rope is **hers.** It belongs to Stacy.

herself ▷ Vivian made cocoa by **herself.** No one helped her
to make it. Vivian made the cocoa for **herself.**
Only Vivian will drink it.

---

hide ▷ To **hide** means to be in a place where **no one
can see you.**
When we played **hide**-and-seek, I **hid** in the
garage. I was **hiding.** I was **hidden. No one
could see me.**

---

high ▷ **High** means **up above.**
A bee flies **high** in the sky.
A bee flies in the sky **up above** us. A bird
flies **higher.** It flies **above** a bee. An airplane
flies **highest.**
It flies **above** the
bee and the bird.

▷ **High** also means
tall.
How **high** am
I? I am four
feet **tall.**

him ➤ Fred's aunt and uncle took Fred on a trip. Fred's aunt and uncle took **him** on a trip.

---

himself ➤ Grover bought new sneakers by **himself.** No one helped him to buy them. Grover bought the sneakers for **himself.** Only Grover will wear the sneakers.

---

his ➤ The yo-yo is Ivan's.
The yo-yo is **his.** It belongs to Ivan.

---

hit ➤ To **hit** means to **strike.** When you **hit** something, you touch it very hard.
The ball I threw **hit** a tree.
The ball I threw **struck** a tree. The ball touched the tree hard.

---

hold ➤ To **hold** means to **put your fingers or arms around** something.
I **hold** my sister's hand when we go to school. I **put my fingers around** her hand. I **held** her hand when we went to school this morning.

---

hole ➤ A **hole** is an **open place that goes into or through** something.
A button has **holes** that go through it.
Swiss cheese has **holes** that go into it.

holiday

holiday ⇨A **holiday** is a special kind of day. On **holidays,** people don't have to go to school or to work. The Fourth of July is a **holiday.** Christmas and Chanukah are also **holidays.**

---

hollow ⇨Hollow means **having an open place inside.**
A bottle is **hollow.**
A bottle **has an open place inside.**

---

home ⇨Your **home** is the **place where you live.**
Holly goes **home** after school. She goes to the **place where she lives.** When she gets **home,** she plays with her friends. Then Holly has dinner with her family. After dinner, she does her **homework** and watches TV. Then Holly goes to sleep.

---

honest ⇨Cliff broke his father's hammer. His father asked if Cliff knew who broke it. Cliff said, "I broke it." Cliff **did what was good.** He **told the truth.** He **did not lie.** He was **honest.**

---

honey ⇨Honey is a sweet, sticky food made by bees. Bees eat the **honey** they make. People and animals also like to eat **honey. Honey** on toast tastes good.

hook

A **hook** is used to catch, pull, or hold things. A **hook** is always bent. It may be made of metal, wood, or plastic. A **hook** is used to catch fish. A coat **hook** is used to hold coats and other clothes.

To **hook** means to **catch a thing** on something shaped like a hook.
My sweater is **hooked** on a branch.
My sweater is **caught** on a branch.

---

hop

To **hop** means to **jump on one foot.**
Lorelei can **hop** far.
Lorelei can **jump on one foot** from one end of the room to the other.

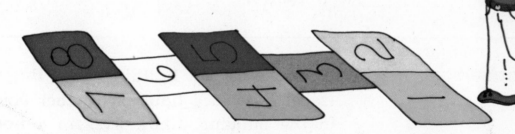

horn

A **horn** is something that cars, trucks, and buses have that goes "honk" or "beep." When you hear the sound a **horn** makes, you know that a car or truck or bus is coming.

A **horn** is also a kind of musical instrument.
Horns are made of a yellow metal, called brass. To play a **horn,** you blow into it.

A **horn** is also something hard that grows above the eyes of some animals. Goats have **horns.**

horse

    horse   ▶A **horse** is a large animal with four legs. **Horses** have long, strong legs that make them fast runners. They are used to carry people and things. A small **horse** is called a pony. A young **horse** is called a colt.

---

    hot   ▶**Hot** means the **opposite of cold.** A fire is **hot.** Ice is cold.

---

    hour   ▶An **hour** is an amount of time. A day is twenty-four **hours** long. The numbers on a clock mean **hours.**

---

    house   ▶Your **house** is the **building you live in.** Isabel lives in a **house.** No other families live in the building. Clark lives in a **house.** One other family also lives in his building.

---

    how   ▶**How** did you get to the beach? **What way** did you go? Which road did you use?

                  ▶**How** did you come from school? Did you walk, or ride the bus?

                  ▶**How many** cookies will you eat? **What number** of cookies will you eat?

                  ▶Myrna told us **how** she won the game. Myrna told us **the way in which** she won.

hug ➤ To **hug** means to **put your arms around** someone or something **and squeeze** them.
I like to **hug** my teddy bear.
I like to **put my arms around** it **and squeeze**

---

human ➤ A **human** is a **person**. You are a **human**. Your pet turtle is not a **human**.

---

hundred

➤ A **hundred** is a number. A **hundred** is also written as **100**. Four quarters make one **hundred** cents.

---

hungry ➤ To be **hungry** means to **want to eat**.
Jethro is **hungry**.
Jethro **wants to eat**.

---

hurry ➤ To **hurry** means to **do** something **very fast**.
Meg **hurried** to get to school on time.
Meg **walked very fast** to get to school on time.

---

hurt ➤ To **hurt** means to **feel pain**.
My thumb **hurts** because I hit it with the hammer. I **feel pain** in my thumb.

➤ To **hurt** also means to **make someone feel pain**.
I **hurt** Lyle when I stepped on his foot.
I **made** Lyle **feel pain** when I stepped on his foot.

I ⇨I is the word you use when talking or writing about yourself. Geraldine wrote:

I love to ice skate. **I am** glad that **I'm** going skating today. **I have** a new pair of skates **I've** never used before. **I will** skate all day, but **I'll** be home for dinner.

---

ice ⇨Ice is **very cold and hard water.** It is not easy to walk on **ice.**

---

ice cream ⇨Ice cream is a very cold food made from milk, cream, and sugar. **Ice cream** comes in many colors and flavors. Have you ever eaten an **ice cream** cone?

---

if ⇨I can play outdoors **if** it is sunny.
I can play outdoors **when** it is sunny.

⇨Do you know **if** the candy is gone?
Do you know **whether** the candy is gone?

ill

⇨ Ill means **sick,** or **not well.**
Bernice is **ill.** She is **sick.** She is **not well.**
She has a cold.

---

in

⇨ The cow ran **in** the barn.
The cow ran **into** the barn.
The cow ran **inside** the barn.

⇨ We slept **in** the forest. We slept where there was a forest all around us.

⇨ **In** the spring, many plants have flowers.
When it is spring, many plants have flowers.

⇨ I do my arithmetic **in** pencil. I use a pencil to do my arithmetic.

---

insect

⇨ An **insect** is a very small animal. **Insects** are also called **bugs.** A mosquito is an **insect** that bites. A worm is an **insect** that lives in the ground. A cricket is an **insect** that makes squeaking noises. A bee is an **insect** that makes honey. There are many other kinds of **insects** also. Can you name some?

---

inside

⇨ **Inside** is the **opposite of outside.**
This book has an **inside** and an outside. This page is **inside** the cover. The cover is outside. The cover goes around the pages.

instead

➥**Instead** means something is **taking the place** of another thing.

Let's play games **instead** of watching TV.

Let's play games **in place** of watching TV.

---

into

➥The bird went **into** its cage. It went **from the outside to the inside** of its cage.

➥The snow **turned into** rain.

The snow **became** rain.

---

invite

➥To **invite** means to **ask someone to visit** you.

I **invited** my friend to come to see me.

I **asked** my friend **to visit** me.

---

is

➥Tina **is** hungry. **"Is** it dinnertime?" asks Tina. "Dinner **isn't** ready," says Mother. "When **are** we going to eat?" says Tina. "I **am** hungry." Mother says, "I know you **are** hungry, but we must wait for our guests. They **are** coming soon."

---

island

➥An **island** is a piece of **land that has water all around** it.

---

it

➥Lou has a kitten. **It** is black. **It's** called Pinkie because **its** nose is pink. Lou likes to watch the kitten wash **itself.**

Jj

jacket ⇨ A **jacket** is a **short coat**.
Here is a picture of a **jacket**.

jam ⇨ **Jam** is a thick, sweet food. **Jam** is made from sugar and many kinds of fruits.

jar ⇨ A **jar** is a kind of container. You can buy food in **jars.** Peanut butter comes in a **jar.**

jelly ⇨ **Jelly** is a sweet, sticky food that is made from sugar and different kinds of juices. What flavor **jelly** do you like the most?

jet ⇨ A **jet** is a kind of airplane that can fly very fast. **Jets** have no propellers.

job

job ➡ A **job** is **work to do.**
Keeping my pet healthy is my **job.**
Keeping my pet healthy is my **work.**

joke ➡ A **joke** is a **funny story or act.**
Do you know a **joke** to tell me?
Do you know a **funny story** to tell me?

joy ➡ **Joy** is a **very, very happy or glad feeling.**
What makes you feel **joy?**
What makes you **very, very happy?**

juice ➡ **Juice** is the **liquid that comes out of fruit and vegetables** when they are squeezed. What is your favorite kind of **juice?**

jump ➡ To **jump,** or **leap,** means to **use your legs to go up** in the air **and come down on your feet.**
The cow **jumped** over the moon.

just ➡ I have **just** the amount of money I need.
I have **exactly** the amount of money I need.

➡ Donnie **just** missed the school bus.
Donnie missed the the school bus by **a little bit.**

➡ I don't think that's **just!**
I don't think that's **fair!**

K k

kangaroo

A **kangaroo** is a large animal that eats plants. **Kangaroos** have short front legs and large, strong back legs. **Kangaroos** are good jumpers. A mother **kangaroo** carries her babies in a place on the front of her body, called her pouch.

keep

Will you **keep** my money?
Will you **take care of** my money and make sure it is safe?

Uncle Joe gave me a necklace to **keep.**
Uncle Joe gave me a necklace to **have always.**

I **kept** the library book for two weeks.
I **had** the library book for two weeks.

Can you **keep** a secret?
Can you **stop yourself from telling** a secret?

key

A **key** is a tool that is used to open and close the locks on doors and other things. **Keys** are usually made of metal.

A **key** is also the part of a piano that you touch to make music. Piano **keys** are either black or white.

kick

To **kick** means to **use your foot to hit** something.
Cecilia **kicked** the ball.
Cecilia **used her foot to hit** the ball.

kitchen

A **kitchen** is a **room where food is made ready** to eat. In a **kitchen,** you may find a sink, a stove, and a refrigerator. Some **kitchens** also have a table and chairs in them.

kite

A **kite** is a kind of plaything. **Kites** are made of wood that has very little weight, and of paper or cloth. The wind carries a **kite** and makes it fly. A long string for you to hold is tied to the **kite** to keep it from flying away.

knee

Your **knee** is a part of your body. It is the part of your leg that bends. Have you ever fallen down and hurt your **knee?**

knife

A **knife** is a sharp tool that is used to cut things. People are very careful when they use **knives.**

---

knock

To **knock** means to **beat on a door.**
Who's **knocking?** Who's at the door?
Who's **beating on the door?**

To **knock** also means to **bump** into something.
Barney **knocked** into the wall.
Barney **bumped** into the wall.

---

knot

To **knot** means to **tie together** pieces of string, rope, ribbon, or other things.
The ribbons are **knotted.**
The ribbons are **tied together.**

To **knot** also means to make a loop with one end of a piece of rope and put the other end of it through the loop.

A **knot** is the **place where a** string or other **thing is tied.**
There's a **knot** in my shoelace.
There's a **tied place** in my shoelace.

know

To **know** means to **understand** something.
Kelly **knows** how to read.
Kelly **understands** how to read. Kelly has **known** how to read for a long time.

To **know** also means to be **sure of** something.
I **know** the answer. I am **sure of** the answer.

ladder

A **ladder** is used to get to a place or thing that is higher than you can reach. **Ladders** are made of metal or wood. To go up a **ladder,** you climb it. Here is a picture of one kind of **ladder.**

lake

A **lake** is a large body of water that has land all around it. You can swim and fish in **lakes.** You can also go for boat rides on **lakes.**

lamp

A **lamp** is a kind of furniture that is used to make a dark place light. **Lamps** have electric light bulbs inside them. When you turn a **lamp** on, the bulb lights up.

land

Land is the part of our world that is not water. Land is made of soil, sand, rocks, and other things. When you sit on the grass, you sit on a piece of **land.**

large

➥ **Large** means **very big,** or **not small.**
An elephant is **large.** It is **very big.**
No other animal is **larger.** The elephant
is the **largest** animal in the world.

---

last

➥ To **come last** means to **follow** other things.
Ten **comes last.**
Ten **follows** the other numbers.

1 2 3 4 5 6 7 8 9 10

➥ The **last** of a thing means there are **no more.**
I ate the **last** plum. There are **no more** plums.

➥ To **last** means to **go on** for a time.
Summer vacation **lasts** two months.
Summer vacation **goes on** for two months.

---

late

➥ **Late** means the **last part** of something.
We arrived **late** in the day.
We arrived in the **last part** of the day.

➥ **Late** means something happening **after the usual time.**
Lunch will be **late.** It will be ready **after the usual time.**

---

laugh

➥ To **laugh** means to **make a special sound when you see or hear something funny.**
I'm **laughing** because that joke is funny.

➥ A **laugh** is the **sound people make when they see or hear something funny.**
I heard a **laugh.** Someone said "ha-ha."

lay   ➤To **lay** something means to **put** it **down**.
We **laid** the cloth on the grass.
We **put** the cloth **down** on the grass.

---

lead   ➤To **lead** means to **show others how to go someplace or do something.**
A mother duck **leads** her chicks to the water.
A mother duck **shows** her chicks **how to get to** the water. The chicks follow their mother.
She is a good **leader**.

---

leaf   ➤A **leaf** is a part of a plant. **Leaves** come in many shapes and colors.

lean   ➤To **lean** means to **rest, or put, one thing against another.**
Gail is **leaning** on the fence.
Gail is **resting** on the fence.

---

leap   ➤To **leap** means to **jump.**
We saw a frog **leap.** We saw it **jump.**
It **leapt** into the water.

➤A **leap** is a **jump.**
The grasshopper made a big **leap.**
The grasshopper made a big **jump.**

learn

To **learn** means to **come to know** things.
I have **learned** to add numbers.
I have **come to know** how to add numbers.

---

leave

To **leave** means to **go away from** a place or thing.
On our vacation, we **leave** home.
On our vacation, we **go away from** home.

I **left** my pets at home. I **went away from** my pets. They stayed at home.

---

left

Left is the **opposite of right.**
Archie has a pumpkin at his **left** side.
Rita has a parrot on her **left** hand.

---

leg

Your **legs** are parts of your body. You use them to stand, walk, run, and jump. At the end of each **leg,** you have a foot.

---

lemon

A **lemon** is a yellow fruit that grows on a tree. **Lemons** taste sour. When you mix **lemon** juice with water and sugar, you make lemonade. Do you like the taste of lemonade?

length   ➤ The **length** of something is how **long** it is. What is the **length** of the worm? How **long** is it? It is five inches in **length.**

less   ➤ **Less** means a **smaller amount** of something.
I have **less** soda than you do.
I have a **smaller amount** of soda than you do.

➤ **Less** also means to **take away** something.
Five **less** four is one.
Five **take away** four is one.
The sign − means **less.**

5−4=1

let   ➤ Will your dad **let** you come with us?
Will your dad **allow** you to come with us?

➤ **Let's** play a game. **Let us** play a game.

lettuce   ➤ **Lettuce** is a vegetable with big green leaves. We eat **lettuce** in salads and sandwiches.

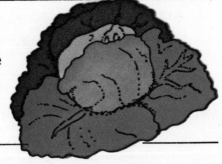

library   ➤ A **library** is a place where there are many books. You can take books out of a **library** if you make sure to bring them back.

lid   ➤ A **lid** is a **cover** for something. Many jars and other containers have **lids.**

lie

➪ To **lie** means to **stretch out** on something.
Cliff is **lying** on the bed. He is **stretched out** on the bed. He has **lain** on it all day.

➪ To **lie** also means to **not tell the truth.**
Some people **lie.** They **don't tell the truth.**

➪ A **lie** is something said that is **not true.**
"I told a **lie**," said Jolene. "I said something that is **not true.**"

---

lift

➪ To **lift** means to **pick up,** or **raise,** something.
A cup is easy to **lift.**
A cup is easy to **pick up. Raising** a cup is easy.

---

light

➪ **Light** means **not dark.**
When the sun shines, the sky is **light.**
When the sun shines, the sky is **not dark.**

This is **light** green and **dark** green.

➪ The **light** is a **place that is not dark.**
Please read your book in the **light.**
Please read **where it is not dark.**

➪ To **light** means to **make light** in a dark place.
The lamp **lit** the dark room.
The lamp **made light** in the dark room.

➪ **Light** also means **having little weight.**
A feather is **light.**
It **has little weight.** It is **not heavy.**

like

like

To **like** something means that it **pleases you.**
I **like** to draw and paint pictures. It **pleases me** to draw and paint pictures.

Like also means that something is **almost the same** as another thing.
Libby swims **like** a fish.
Libby swims **almost as well** as a fish.

line

A **line** is a **long, thin mark** made with a pen, pencil, crayon, or other writing tool.
Here are some colored **lines.**

A **line** is a **rope, string, or wire.**
Telephone poles have **lines** between them.
Telephone poles have **wires** between them.

A **line** is a **row** of people or things.
Here is a **line** of stars. They are all in a **row.**

lion

A **lion** is a large and very strong animal.
Lions are good hunters. When a **lion** makes a sound, it goes "ROAR."

liquid

A **liquid** is something that flows when it is poured. Water and milk are **liquids.** A **liquid** is also called a **fluid.**

listen ➧To **listen** means to **make sure you hear and understand** what is being said.

"Shhhh," said Edna. "I am **listening** to my teacher speak. I am **making sure I hear and understand** what she says."

---

little ➧**Little** means **small**, or **not big**.
Bugs are **little**.
Bugs are **small**. They are **not big**.

➧A **little** means a **small amount** of something.
Would you like a **little** tea? Yes, thank you, I would like a **small amount** of tea.

---

live  ➧To **live** means to be **alive**, or **not dead**.
This plant is **living**.
This plant is **alive**. It is green and healthy.

➧To **live** somewhere means to **have a place to eat, sleep, work, and play**.
I **live** in a red house. It is **the place where I sleep, eat, work, and play**.

---

loaf ➧A **loaf** is a kind of shape. Bread is baked in the shape of a **loaf**.

---

lock  ➧A **lock** is used to keep things closed, or locked. To open and close many kinds of **locks**, you need a key.

long

long

➠ **Long** means **not short.**
The blue string is **long.**
The blue string is **not short.** The red string is **longer.** The green string is **longest.**

look

➠ To **look** means to **use your eyes to see** someone or something.
I **looked** at myself in the mirror.
I **used my eyes to see** myself in the mirror.

➠ To **look** also means to **try to see or find** someone or something.
We **looked** for four-leaf clovers.
We **tried to find** four-leaf clovers.

➠ To **look** also means to **seem to be** something.
Leroy **looks** sad. Leroy **seems** sad.

loose

➠ **Loose** means **not tight.**
I have a **loose** tooth. It wiggles when I touch it. It is **not tight.** When my new tooth comes in, it will be tight. It will not wiggle.

lose

➠ To **lose** means to **not win.**
Our team is **losing** the game.
Our team is **not winning** the game.

➠ To **lose** something means to **not be able to find** it.
Did you **lose** your mittens?
Were you **not able to find** your mittens?
The mittens are **lost.**

loud
➤ **Loud** means that a sound is **not soft,** or **strong.**
The music was **loud.** It was **strong.**
The music was **not soft.**

---

love
➤ To **love** someone means to **like** him or her **very, very much.** When you **love** a person, you want to do good things for them.

---

low
➤ **Low** means **short,** or **not high or tall.**
The grass on the lawn is **short.**
The grass on the lawn is **not tall.** When it grows high, we cut it to make it **short** again.

➤ **Low** also means that a sound is **soft,** or **not loud.**
A whisper is **low.**
A whisper is a **soft** sound.
A whisper is **not loud.**

---

lunch
➤ **Lunch** is the meal we eat in the middle of the day. We eat **lunch** between breakfast and dinner. What did you eat for **lunch** today?

➤ To **lunch** means to **eat lunch.**
Faye is **lunching** at home today.
Faye is **eating lunch** at home today.

Mm

machine

➡ A **machine** helps people to do work. A **machine** has parts that can move. Some **machines** have motors that make their parts move. A car is a **machine** that can carry people and things. A sewing **machine** helps people to make clothes.

---

mail

➡ **Mail** is letters, birthday cards, postcards, and other written things that people send to your home. Letters and other pieces of **mail** that you get have your name and address and a stamp on them. The person who brings, or delivers, your **mail** is called a letter carrier.

➡ To **mail** something means to send a letter or other piece of mail to someone. When you **mail** a letter to a person, you put his or her name and address and a stamp on the letter. Then you take it to the post office or drop it in a mailbox. A letter carrier then delivers the letter to the person.

make

➪ Chester **made** a sand castle.
Chester **built** a sand castle.

➪ We are **making** a sandwich.
We are **putting together** a sandwich.

➪ The cut on my finger **made** me cry.
The cut on my finger **caused me** to cry.
I cried **because of** the cut on
my finger.

➪ Lois delivers newspapers
to **make** money.
Lois delivers newspapers to **earn** money.

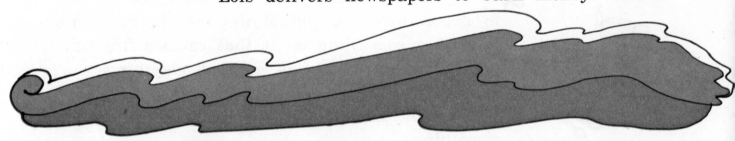

make believe ➪ To **make believe** means to **pretend,** to **imagine,**
or to **play at being** something.
We **made believe** we were pirates.
We **pretended** we were pirates.
We **imagined** we were pirates.
We **played at being** pirates.

➪ **Make-believe** means **not real,** or **imaginary.**
A dragon is a **make-believe** animal.
A dragon is an **imaginary** animal. Dragons
are **not real** animals. They live only in
stories.

man

➪ Dwight's father is a **man.** Dwight's uncle and
grandfather are **men.** Dwight is a boy. When he
grows up, he will be a **man.**

many

many

Many means a **large number** of persons or things.

Our garden has **many** flowers.

Our garden has a **large number** of flowers.

march

To **march** means to **walk in time to music,** or **to walk with other people.**

The band **marched** down the street.

The band **walked in time to music** down the street.

match

A **match** is a stick of wood or paper that is used to make fire. One end of the **match,** called the head, has something on it that catches fire when you scratch it. **Matches** are not playthings.

To **match** means to **be alike,** or **equal to** something.

Which two pictures **match?**

Which two pictures **are alike?**

Which number **matches** the amount of strawberries?

Which number **is equal to** the amount of strawberries?

114

may

➡ **May** I go to the party?
Will you allow me to go to the party?

➡ We **may** go hiking.
Possibly we will go hiking.
Perhaps we will go hiking.

---

maybe

➡ **Maybe** it will snow today.
Perhaps it will snow today. I'm not sure whether it will snow today.

---

me

➡ "The blue scarf belong to **me**," said Kaye. "Mother made it for **me**. I take the scarf to school with **me**. It keeps **me** warm. Do you think it looks pretty on **me**?" asked Kaye.

---

mean

➡ Big **means** not small.
Big is **another way of saying** not small.

➡ The sign + **means** to add.
The sign + **tells you** to add.

➡ A **mean** person is someone who is not kind to other people and things.

---

measure

➡ To **measure** means to **find the size** of something.
"I **measured** my height," said Pedro. "I **found the size** of my body in inches."

melt

To **melt** means to **change from something hard to something liquid.**
My ice cream has **melted.**
My ice cream has **changed from something hard** and cold **to something liquid** and warm.

---

mend

To **mend** means to **fix,** or **repair,** something.
I **mended** the hole in my sock.
I **fixed** the hole in my sock.

---

merry

Merry means **happy** and **jolly** and **gay.**
"**Merry** Christmas!" cried Santa. "Be **happy** and **jolly** and **gay!**"

---

metal

Metal comes from inside the earth. **Metals** are used to make things. Airplanes are made of **metal.** Gold and iron are two kinds of **metal.**

---

middle

The **middle** of something is its **center.**
This candy has a cherry in the **middle.**
This candy has a cherry in the **center.**

---

might

Ethan **might** win a prize.
Possibly Ethan **will** win a prize.
Maybe Ethan **will** win a prize.

---

milk

Milk is a food. It is a white liquid. The **milk** we drink comes from cows. **Milk** and chocolate cookies make a very good snack.

mind

➤ Your **mind** is a part of your body that you cannot see. You use your **mind** to think and to remember things.

➤ Do you **mind** if we leave soon?
Do you **care** if we leave soon?

➤ Please **mind** what I say. Please **obey** me.

➤ **Mind** your good clothes.
Be careful with your good clothes.

mine

➤ **Mine** means **belongs to me.**
"The blue wagon is **mine**," said Flora. "It **belongs to me.**"

minus

➤ **Minus** means **less,** or **take away** something.
Ten **minus** three is seven.
Ten **take away** three is seven.

10-3=7

The sign — means **minus.**

minute

➤ A **minute** is an amount of time. There are sixty minutes in one hour. The long hand on a **clock** shows **minutes.**

mirror

➤ A **mirror** is something shiny in which you can see yourself. Most **mirrors** are made of glass. A **mirror** is also called a **looking glass.**

117

mistake To make a **mistake** means to **choose something** that is **wrong.**

Amelia made a **mistake** when she **chose** the **wrong** answer.

---

mitten A **mitten** is a warm covering for your hand. A **mitten** has a place to put your thumb. It has another, larger, place to put the rest of your fingers.

---

mix To **mix** means to **stir together** two or more things.

Mix red and blue to make purple.
Stir together red and blue to make purple.

---

money **Money** is used to buy things. A penny, a nickel, and a dime are pieces of metal **money** called coins. A dollar bill is a piece of paper **money.**

---

monkey A **monkey** is an animal that has long arms and a long tail. **Monkeys** can use their tails to hold things. Have you ever seen a **monkey** in a zoo?

---

month A **month** is an amount of time. Most **months** are thirty-one days long. The twelve **months** of the year are January, February, March, April, May, June, July, August, September, October, November, and December. In which **month** is your birthday?

moon

➡ The **moon** is the largest bright thing in the nighttime sky. The **moon** is very far from the earth. Sometimes the **moon** can be seen in the daytime. The **moon** is round, but at certain times only a part of the **moon** can be seen. Then the **moon** may look like this.

more

➡ **More** means a **bigger amount** of something.
I have **more** crayons than you have.
I have a **bigger amount** of crayons than you have.

➡ **More** also means **another** of something.
Would you like **more** fruit?
Would you like **another** piece of fruit?

morning

➡ The **morning** is the **first part of the day.**
The sun rises in the **morning.**
The sun rises in the **first part of the day.**

most

➡ **Most** means the **biggest amount** of something.
Eric has the **most** jelly beans.
Eric has the **biggest amount** of jelly beans.

➡ **Most** also means **more than other things.**
I enjoy summer the **most.**
I enjoy summer **more than** fall, winter, or spring.

mother

mother

A **mother** is a woman who has a child. A **mother** is sometimes called **Mom** or **Mommy**. You are your **mother's** child.

motor

A **motor** is a kind of machine that makes things move. The **motor** in a motorcycle makes it move. A **motor** is also called an **engine**.

mountain

A **mountain** is a tall place on the earth. **Mountains** are made of soil and rocks. Some **mountains** always have snow on their tops.

mouse

A **mouse** is a small, furry animal. **Mice** have thin tails and sharp little teeth.

mouth

Your **mouth** is a part of your body. Inside your **mouth** you have teeth and a tongue. You use your **mouth** to eat and to talk and to breathe.

move

To **move** means to **go from one place to another**.
A boat **moves**.
A boat **goes from one place to another**.

To **move** also means to **make any kind of action**.
I can **move** my hands.
I can **make actions** with my hands. I can clap, wave, and do other things with my hands.

much   Much means a **large amount** of something.
A farmer spends **much** time in his garden.
A farmer spends a **large amount** of time in his garden.

mud   Mud is **dirt and water mixed together. Mud** is fun to play with when you are outdoors.

museum   A **museum** is a place where people can go to see and learn about interesting things. In an art **museum,** you can see pictures, statues, and other things made by people. In other **museums,** you can learn about the stars or the different kinds of animals from around the world.

music   Music is the **pleasing sounds** people make when they sing, or play pianos, drums, or other musical instruments. When birds sing, we say they make **music.**

my   My means **something that belongs to me.**
These are **my** shoes.
The shoes **belong to me.**
The shoes are mine.

myself   "I drew a picture of **myself,**" said Ned. "It is a picture of me. I drew it by **myself.** No one helped me to draw it. I drew it for **myself.** The picture is for me."

121

Nn

nail

⇨ Your **nails** are parts of your body. They are the hard places at the ends of your fingers and toes.

⇨ A **nail** is used to hold pieces of wood or other things together. **Nails** are usually made of metal. To make a **nail** go into wood, you hit it with a hammer.

name

⇨ A **name** is a word that means a certain person or thing.

"My **name** is Herbie," said Herbie. "When someone says 'Herbie,' I know they are speaking to me."

What is the **name** of this kind of bird? The **name** of this kind of bird is cardinal. This kind of bird is **called** a cardinal.

narrow

⇨ **Narrow** means **not wide.**

A pencil makes a **narrow** line. The line a pencil makes is **not wide.** It is **thin.**

near

➡ **Near** means **close,** or **not far.**
The park is **near** my house.
The park is **close** to my house. It is **not far** from my house to the park.

---

nearly

➡ **Nearly** means **almost.**
Jared is **nearly** eight years old.
Jared is **almost** eight years old.

---

neck

➡ Your **neck** is a part of your body. It is the part of your body between your head and your shoulders.

---

need

➡ To **need** something means you **must have** it.
I **need** a new coat.
I **must have** a new coat. My old coat is too small for me.

---

needle

➡ A **needle** is used for sewing. **Needles** are long, thin pieces of metal. One end of the **needle** is sharp and pointy. In the other end of the needle is a small hole called an eye. When you thread a **needle,** you put a piece of thread through the eye.

neighbor

➡ **Neighbors** are **people who live near one another.**
Georgia and Ross are **neighbors.** They **live near one another.**

neither ➡ Neither means **not each one of two** things.
Neither answer is right.
Not one of the two answers is right. Both answers are wrong.

---

never ➡ Never means **not at any time.**
A cat will **never** bark like a dog.
A cat will **not at any time** bark like a dog.
A cat will **not ever** bark like a dog.

---

new ➡ Let's play a **new** game.
Let's play a **different** game. Let's play a game that we have never played before.

➡ I have a **new** hat. I just bought it.

---

next ➡ To be **next** to something means to be **near** it, just **before** it, or just **after** it.
Six comes **next** to seven.
Six comes just **before** seven.

$$4\ 5\ 6\ 7\ 8$$

Z comes **next** to Y.
Z comes just **after** Y.

$$X\ Y\ Z$$

---

nickel ➡ A **nickel** is a piece of money. It is made of metal. A **nickel** is the same as **five cents.** It is also written as **5¢.** Two **nickels** make one dime.

124

night ➤ The **night** is the **time when it is dark outside.**

Stars twinkle at **night.**

Stars twinkle **when it is dark outside.**

---

nine ➤ **Nine** is a number. It is also written as **9.** Here are **nine** peanuts.

nineteen ➤ **Nineteen** is a number. It is also written as **19.** How many jelly beans can you count?

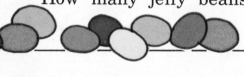

ninety ➤ **Ninety** is a number. It is also written as **90.** Nine dimes make **ninety** cents.

no ➤ I asked Louise, "Is your name Patsy?" Louise said, "**No,** my name is **not** Patsy."

➤ Arty has **no** money.
Arty does **not** have any money. He has none.

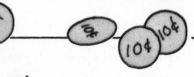

---

nobody ➤ **Nobody** means **no person.**

Nobody won the game.

No person won the game.

No one won the game.

noise

➤A **noise** is a **sound that is not pleasing.**
That machine makes **noise.**
That machine makes **sounds that are not pleasing.** That machine is noisy.

➤A **noise** is also any **sound.**
What is that **noise** I hear?
What is that **sound** I hear?

---

none

➤**None** means **no person or thing.**
None of the work is done.
Not any of the work is done.
No work is done.

---

noon

➤**Noon** is the time of day between the morning and the afternoon. It is **noon** when the sun is highest in the sky and both hands on a clock point to twelve.

---

no one

➤**No one** means **no person.**
No one wanted to leave the park.
No person wanted to leave the park.
Not anybody wanted to leave the park.

---

nose

➤Your **nose** is a part of your body. It is in the center of your face. You use your **nose** to breathe and to smell things.

not

➤**Not** means the same as **no.**
Would you like a peach?
No, thank you. I do **not** want a peach.

notice ➡ To **notice** something means to **see** it.
Did you **notice** my drawing?
Did you **see** my drawing?
Did you **look at** my drawing?

---

now ➡ **Now** means **at this time.**
I hear the train coming **now.**
I hear the train coming **at this time.**

---

number ➡ A **number** shows **how many** things there are.
What is the **number** of blocks?
How many blocks are there?
The **number** of blocks is three.
The **number** is .

These are the **numbers** from one to twenty.

1 2 3 4 5 6 7 8 9 10 11 12 13 14 15 16 17 18 19 20

---

nurse ➡ A **nurse** is a person who takes care of people when they are ill.

---

nut ➡ A **nut** is a fruit that grows on some kinds of trees and bushes. Many **nuts** are good to eat. **Nuts** have a hard outside, called a shell. We eat the part of the **nut** inside the shell. Walnuts and peanuts are two kinds of **nuts** we eat.

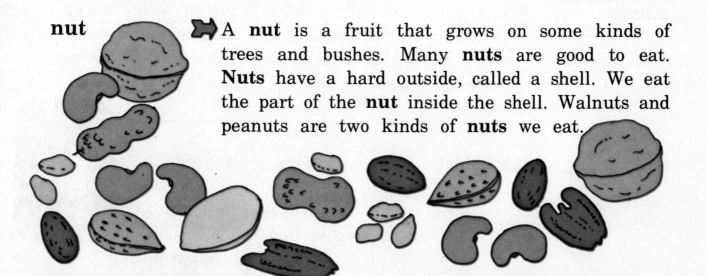

1 Oo

oar An **oar** is used to make a boat move. **Oars** are usually made of wood. When you use an **oar** to make a boat move, you are rowing.

obey To **obey** means to **do what you are told** to do. The sign in the library said "QUIET." Gene **obeyed** the sign. Gene was quiet. Gene **did what he was told** to do.

object 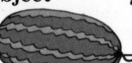 An **object** is a **thing**. A car is an **object**. A watermelon, a doll, and a key are **objects**.

ocean An **ocean** is a very large body of water. **Ocean** water is salty. Ships can sail across the **ocean**. Fish and other animals live in **oceans**. An **ocean** is also called a **sea**.

o'clock **O'clock** means the **time that a clock shows**.

When it is four **o'clock**, the **clock shows time** by having the big hand on the twelve and the little hand on the four.

octopus

An **octopus** is an animal that lives on the bottom of the sea. An **octopus** has eight arms.

of

I have a toy **of** Donna's.
I have a toy that **belongs to** Donna.

We eat the fruit **of** trees.
We eat the fruit **grown by** trees.

Some chairs are made **of** wood.
Some chairs are made **from** wood.

May I have a glass **of** milk?
May I have a glass **filled with** milk?

Do you know the story **of** Snow White?
Do you know the story **about** Snow White?

off

The radio is **off**. The radio is **not on.** There are no sounds coming from the radio.

Norman took his boots **off**.
Norman took his boots **from** his feet.

often

Laura has been to camp **often.**
Laura has been to camp **many times.**

How **often** do you go to school? I go to school **often.** I go five times a week.

old

old

⇨My grandma is **old**. She is **not young.**

⇨Eloise is two years **old**. Her **age** is two years.
Dean is five years **old**. He is **older** than Eloise.
Lynn is six years **old**. She is **oldest.**

⇨My sneakers are **old**. They are **not new.**
I have had them a long time.

---

on

⇨My pet bird can sit **on** my finger.
My pet bird can sit **upon** my finger.

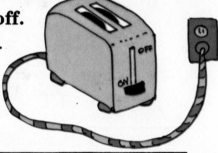

⇨We went to the park **on**
Saturday.
We went to the park **when** it
was Saturday.

⇨The toaster is **on**. It is **not off.**
The toaster is making toast.

⇨Is your hat **on?** Are you
wearing your hat?

---

once

⇨I have been to a zoo **once.**
I have been to a zoo **one time.**

⇨Please come **at once.**
Please come **now.** Come **immediately.**

⇨We all laughed **at once.**
We all laughed **at the same time.**

⇨Robin Hood lived **once upon a time.**
Robin Hood lived a **long time ago.**

orange

one　　　　⮞ **One** is a number. **One** is also written as **1.**
　　　　　　Here is **one** pineapple.

only　　　　⮞ **Only** Adam knew the answer. Adam **alone** knew
　　　　　　the answer. No one else knew the answer.

　　　　　　⮞ I ate **only** one of the doughnuts.
　　　　　　I ate **just** one of the doughnuts.

open　　　　⮞ **Open** means **not closed.**
　　　　　　Ruben's eyes are **open.**
　　　　　　His eyes are **not closed.** Ruben is awake.

　　　　　　What time does school **open?**
　　　　　　What time does school **begin?**

　　　　　　⮞ To **open** something means to **unclose** it.
　　　　　　Please **open** your book.
　　　　　　Please **unclose** your book so you can do your
　　　　　　lesson.

or　　　　⮞ Do you want milk **or** juice?
　　　　　　Do you want milk? Do you want juice? You may
　　　　　　have one **or** the other. Which one do you want?

orange　　　　⮞ **Orange** is a color. This is **orange**.

　　　　　　⮞ An **orange** is a fruit. **Oranges**
　　　　　　grow on trees. Do you like to
　　　　　　drink **orange** juice?

other

other

➡️ Norma has one glove. She lost the **other**.

➡️ One egg is broken. The **other** eggs are not.
The **others** are not.
All but one of the eggs are not broken.

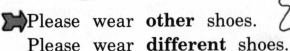

➡️ Please wear **other** shoes.
Please wear **different** shoes.

➡️ Are there any **other** grapes?
Are there any **more** grapes?

ought

➡️ Barry **ought** to be home by now.
Barry **should** be home by now. He was expected to be home by now.

➡️ I **ought** to keep my room clean.
I **should** keep my room clean. It is my job to keep my room clean.

our

➡️ **Our** means **belonging to us**.
Our puppy **belongs to us**. The puppy is **ours**.
We take care of it **ourselves**. No one helps us to take care of **our** puppy.

out

➡️ I poured the milk **out** of the carton.
I poured the milk **from** the carton.

➡️ The sun came **out**. It moved from behind a cloud to where it could be seen.

132

outdoors   The **outdoors** is every place that is **not inside** a building. When you go **outside** to play, you go **outdoors.**

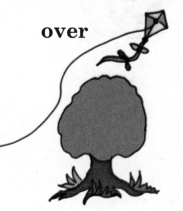

over   The kite flew **over** the tree.
The kite flew **above** the tree.

There is a blanket **over** my bed.
There is a blanket **covering** my bed.

A boat goes **over** water.
A boat goes **across** water.

Heather has **over** fifty cents.
Heather has **more than** fifty cents.

When is school **over?** When does it **end?**

Geoffrey knocked the glass **over.** He knocked the glass down.

When you turn something **over,** you turn it to its other side.

owl   An **owl** is a kind of bird that sleeps during the day. **Owls** hunt for food at night.

own   To **own** something means to have it **belong** to you.
I **own** red socks. They **belong** to me.
Kris **owns** blue socks. Her socks **belong** to her. Kris and I **own** our socks.

Pp

package

➡️ A **package** is a box that has been wrapped in paper. When we don't know what is inside the box, we call it a surprise **package.**

pail

➡️ A **pail** is used to hold water and other things. Do you have a **pail** to play with at the beach? A **pail** is also called a **bucket.**

paint

➡️ **Paint** is a colored liquid that is used to put color on paper, wood, and other things.

➡️ To **paint** means to **put paint on** a thing.
May I help to **paint** the chair?
May I help to **put paint on** the chair?

paintbrush

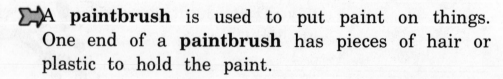

➡️ A **paintbrush** is used to put paint on things. One end of a **paintbrush** has pieces of hair or plastic to hold the paint.

pan

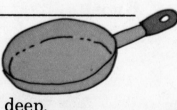

➡️ A **pan** is a container used for cooking. Most **pans** are round and made of metal. **Pans** are not very deep.

pants

Pants are a kind of clothes. Long **pants** go from your waist to your ankles. Short **pants** cover only part of your legs.

paper

Paper is used to write and draw on. **Paper** is made from the wood of trees, or from other plants. This book is made of **paper.**

parade

A **parade** is a **group of people marching** together. Some **parades** have musicians and people dressed in colorful clothes. In some **parades** there are also clowns and animals.

parakeet

A **parakeet** is a small bird. It may be blue, green, yellow, or white. **Parakeets** make good pets.

parent

A **parent** is a person who has a child. Your **parents** are your mother and father.

park

A **park** is a place outdoors that everyone may visit. **Parks** usually have many trees and other plants. In some **parks** people can picnic and play games. In other **parks** there are lakes for people to swim in and go boating on. Some **parks** also give animals a place to live.

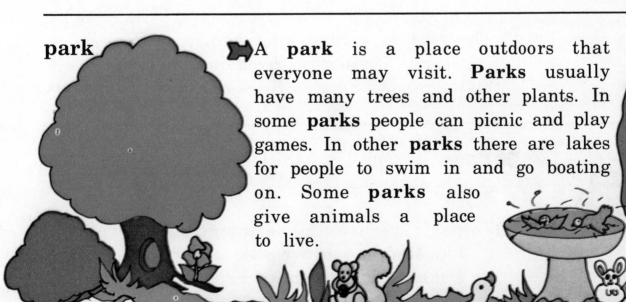

parrot

➤ A **parrot** is a bird that can be taught to say words. **Parrots** come in pretty colors.

part

➤ A **part** is **one of the smaller things** that together make a larger, whole thing.

A room is **part** of a house.

A room is **one of the smaller things** that make a whole house.

pass

➤ To **pass** means to **go by** something.

We **passed** the store.

We **went by** the store.

➤ To **pass** also means to **hand** something to a person.

Please **pass** the butter to me.

Please **hand** the butter to me.

Please **give** the butter to me.

past

➤ The **past** is a **time long ago.**

George Washington lived in the **past.**

George Washington lived in a **time long ago.**

paste

➤ **Paste** is something thick that is used to make things stick together.

➤ To **paste** means to **make things stick together.**

I **pasted** the two pieces of paper.

I **made the pieces** of paper **stick together.**

path ➡️ A **path** is a small road that people and animals can walk on. Have you ever walked on a **path** through the woods?

paw ➡️ A **paw** is a foot of a four-legged animal. A **paw** has nails, or claws. Cats and dogs and bears have **paws.**

pea  ➡️ A **pea** is a small, round vegetable that grows on a vine. **Peas** grow together in a case called a pod.

peach ➡️ A **peach** is a fuzzy yellow and pink fruit that grows on a tree.

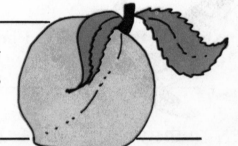

peanut ➡️ A **peanut** is a kind of bean that looks and tastes like a nut. **Peanuts** grow under the ground. Elephants like to eat **peanuts.**

peanut butter ➡️ **Peanut butter** is a sweet, sticky food that is made from peanuts.

pear ➡️ A **pear** is a fruit that grows on a tree. **Pears** may be green or yellow with brown and pink spots.

pen

pen
➤A **pen** is a tool used for writing. Inside a **pen** is a liquid called ink. When you write with a **pen** you put ink on paper.

pencil
➤A **pencil** is a tool used for writing. **Pencils** are made of wood. Inside the wood is something that can make marks on paper and others things.

penguin
➤A **penguin** is a bird that can swim but cannot fly. Most **penguins** are black and white or gray and white. **Penguins** live in cold places.

penny
➤A **penny** is a piece of money. It is made of metal. A **penny** is the same as a **cent**. A **penny** is also written as **1¢**.

people
➤**People** are **humans**. All **persons** are **people**. Animals, plants, and other things are not **people**.

perhaps
➤**Perhaps** we will go fishing today.
Maybe we will go fishing today. I'm not sure if we will go fishing today.

pet
➤A **pet** is an animal that you take care of and play with. People often give names to their **pets**. Do you have a **pet**? What kind of animal is it? Does it have a name?

piano

➡ A **piano** is a large musical instrument. Most of a **piano** is made of wood. To play a **piano,** you touch its black and white keys.

pick

➡ To **pick** means to **choose,** or to say you want one thing from many things.
I **picked** the red dress.
I **chose** the red dress. There were many dresses, but I wanted the red one.

picnic

➡ A **picnic** is a **meal** that **you eat outdoors.**
We had a **picnic** on the beach. We had lunch on the beach.

➡ To **picnic** means to **eat outdoors.**
We like **picnicking.**
We like **eating outdoors.**

picture

➡ A **picture** is **something** that a person has **painted or drawn.** Here are some **pictures.**

➡ A **picture** is also the shapes and colors you see on a special kind of paper when you use a camera. A **picture** made by a camera is called a photograph.

pie

pie

→ **Pie** is something to eat. The dough on the outside of a **pie** is called the crust. Inside a **pie** there is a filling. Some **pies** have fillings of meat and vegetables. **Pies** you eat for dessert have sweet fillings of pudding or fruit.

---

piece

→ A **piece** is **one of the smaller things** that together make a larger, whole thing.

May I have a **piece** of the pie?
May I have **one of the smaller parts** that make a whole pie?

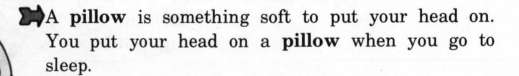

---

pig

→ A **pig** is an animal that you might see on a farm. **Pigs** may be black, white, pink, or brown. People eat the meat of **pigs.** A young **pig** is called a piglet.

pillow

→ A **pillow** is something soft to put your head on. You put your head on a **pillow** when you go to sleep.

---

pilot

→ A **pilot** is a person who steers, or drives, an airplane or a boat.

---

pink

→ **Pink** is a color. This is pink.

To get **pink,** mix red and white.

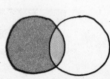

plant ➤A **plant** is something live that grows in dirt, or soil. Plants need sun and water. Trees and flowers are **plants.**

➤To **plant** means to **put seeds into soil** so that they can grow into plants.
  We **planted** pumpkin seeds.
  We **put** pumpkin **seeds into soil.**

---

plate ➤A **plate** is a flat, usually round, dish. We eat food from **plates.**

---

play ➤To **play** means to **have fun.**
  We **played** outside.
  We **had fun** outside.

➤To **play** also means to **make believe.**
  We **played** we were on a boat.
  We **made believe** we were on a boat.
  We **pretended** we were on a boat.

---

playground ➤A **playground** is a place that is made just for people to play in. Some **playgrounds** have swings and slides. Schools and parks often have **playgrounds.**

plaything ➤A **plaything** is a toy, or anything you can play with. A doll is a **plaything.** A ball and a jump rope are also **playthings.** Matches are not **playthings.**

please

Please is a word that is nice to say when you ask for something.

Leslie said, "**Please,** may I have a dog?"

Leslie asked nicely. She said **please.**

To **please** means to **make someone feel good or happy.**

I **pleased** Grandpa by writing to him.

I **made Grandpa feel good.**

To **be pleased** means to **feel good** about something.

Rick **was pleased** because it was his birthday.

Rick **felt good** because it was his birthday.

---

plenty

Anthony has **plenty** of toys.

Anthony has **many** toys.

I have had **plenty** to eat.

I have had **enough** to eat.

I have **plenty** of gum.

I have **more** gum **than I need or want.** You may have some of my gum.

---

pocket

A **pocket** is a place in your clothes that can hold small things. Rose has a red handkerchief in her **pocket.** Do you have any **pockets** in the clothes you are wearing today?

---

pocketbook

A **pocketbook** is a container that people use to carry their money, keys, gum and other things that they use every day.

police officer ➭ A **police officer** is a person who tries to make sure that people are good to other people and obey the law. Some **police officers** wear blue uniforms.

polite ➭ To be **polite** means to be **good to people.** Rudy was being **polite** when he thanked his aunt for giving him a present. Rudy was being good to his aunt.

pond ➭ A **pond** is a small body of water that has land all around it. Frogs and other animals live in some **ponds.**

pony ➭ A **pony** is a kind of horse that does not grow to be very big. Have you ever gone for a ride on a **pony?**

PONY RIDES 15¢

popcorn ➭ **Popcorn** is a food made from kernels of corn. When the kernels get very hot, they "POP" open. Have you ever made **popcorn?**

possible ➭ It is **possible** that it will snow. **Maybe** it will snow.

post office ➭ A **post office** is a building you go to when you want to send letters, packages, and other pieces of mail to another person.

pot  A **pot** is a container used for cooking. **Pots** are usually round and made of metal. You can find many **pots** in a kitchen.

potato A **potato** is a vegetable that is brown or red on the outside and white on the inside. **Potatoes** grow under the ground.

pour To **pour** means to **make liquid move, or flow,** from one place to another.

I **poured** a glass of soda.
I **made the soda move** from the bottle into the glass. The soda **flowed** into the glass.

prepare To **prepare** a meal means to **make food ready** to eat.

I am **preparing** breakfast.
I am **making the food** for breakfast **ready** to eat.

To **prepare** also means to **get ready** to do something.

Dinah **prepared** to go out in the rain.
Dinah put on her rubber boots and took her umbrella with her.

To be **prepared** means to **be ready** to do something.

Are you **prepared** to go camping?
Are you **ready** to go camping? Do you have all the things you need to go camping?

144

present

A **present** is a **gift.**
I have a **present** for you.
I have a **gift** for you. I have
something special to give
to you.

To **be present** means to **be in this place.**
Jody is **present.**
Jody is **in this place.** She is **here.**

The **present** means **this time,** or **now.**
At **present,** it is two o'clock.
Now it is two o'clock.

---

pretend

Pretend means **make-believe,** or **imaginary.**
A unicorn is a **pretend** animal.
A unicorn is a **make-believe** animal.
A unicorn is an **imaginary** animal. Unicorns
live only in stories.

To **pretend** means to **make believe.**
Let's **pretend** to be fire fighters.
Let's **make believe** we are fire fighters.
Let's **play at being** fire fighters.

---

pretty

Pretty means **pleasing.**
Flowers are **pretty.**
Flowers are **pleasing** to look at. I like looking
at flowers. Flowers are also **pretty** to smell.

price

price   ➡The **price** of something is **how much money you need to buy** it.

The **price** of gum is 15¢. Grant needs 15¢ to buy the gum. The gum's **price** is 15¢.

prize   ➡A **prize** is something that you earn when you win a race or game.

promise   ➡A **promise** is what a person says he or she will do.

I made a **promise** to not lie. My **promise** was to not lie. I said I would not lie.

pudding   ➡**Pudding** is a thick, sweet food. **Pudding** comes in many flavors and colors. Do you like butterscotch **pudding?**

puddle   ➡A **puddle** is a small body of liquid. After it rains, there are **puddles** of water in the street.

pull   ➡To **pull** means to **take hold of something and make it come toward you or with you.**
The sign on the door said "PULL."
The sign on the door told me to **take hold** of it **and make it come toward me.**

As I walked, I **pulled** my wagon.
As I walked, I **made it come with me.**

146

pumpkin

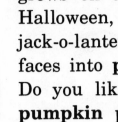
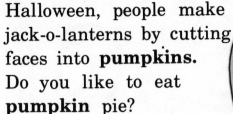

A **pumpkin** is a yellow or orange vegetable that grows on a vine. On Halloween, people make jack-o-lanterns by cutting faces into **pumpkins.** Do you like to eat **pumpkin** pie?

puppet

A **puppet** is a plaything that is made to look like a person or animal. **Puppets** can be made to move. You put your hand inside some **puppets** to move them. Other **puppets** are moved by pulling strings tied to them.

---

purple

Purple is a color. This is **purple**. Mix red and blue to make **purple.**

---

push

To **push** means to **touch something and make it move away** from you **or in front** of you.
Please **push** my swing.
Please **touch** my swing **and make it move away** from you.

Charlene likes to **push** the baby carriage.
Charlene likes **touching** the carriage **and making it move along in front** of her.

---

puzzle

A **puzzle** is a kind of game. **Puzzles** have many pieces. When you do a **puzzle,** you try to fit all the pieces together.

quack   ➤Quack is the **sound that a duck makes.**

➤To **quack** means to **make the sound "quack."** Here are some **quacking** ducks.

quantity   ➤**Quantity** means **how many** there are of a thing. What is the **quantity** of quacking ducks? **How many** quacking ducks are there? What is the **number** of quacking ducks?

quart   ➤A **quart** is an amount of liquid. Have you ever gone to the store to buy a **quart** of milk?

quarter   ➤A **quarter** is a piece of money. It is made of metal. A **quarter** is **twenty-five cents.**

➤A **quarter** is also three or more coins that equal **twenty-five cents. Two dimes and a nickel** make a **quarter.**

quarter

A **quarter** is **one of four parts** of something. Each **quarter** is **the same size** as the others.
We each ate a **quarter** of the orange.
We each ate **one of the four parts** of the orange. Each part was **the same size**.

Kevin had eight walnuts. He ate a **quarter** of them. He ate **one-fourth** of them. Kevin ate two of the eight walnuts.

To **quarter** means to **make something into four parts of the same size**.
Marcie **quartered** a piece of paper.
Marcie **made a piece of paper into four parts of the same size**.

---

question

A **question asks** something.
"How are you today?" is a **question**.
"How are you today?" **asks** how you feel.
The sign **?** means **question**.

---

quick

Quick means **fast,** or **not slow**.
Earl won the race because he was **quick**.
Earl won the race because he was **fast**.

---

quiet

To be **quiet** means to **make very little, or no, sound**.
Please be **quiet. Make no sound.**

---

quit

To **quit** means to **stop doing** something.
Why did you **quit** the game?
Why did you **stop playing** the game?

Rr

rabbit

➡ A rabbit is a small furry animal. **Rabbits** have long ears. A **rabbit** is also called a **bunny.**

race

➡ To **race** means to **move very fast.**
The car **raced** down the road.
The car **moved very fast** down the road.

➡ To **race** also means to **try to win.**
I'll **race** you to school!
I'll **try to beat** you to school! If I get to school first, I win!

➡ A **race** is a **contest** to see who is fastest.
Who will win the **race?**
Who will win the **contest?** Who will be fastest? Who will be first?

radio

➡ A **radio** sends and receives sounds. You can hear these sounds only when your **radio** is on. When you listen to a **radio** you hear music, or people talking or singing.

150

railroad → A **railroad** is trains, and the roads, called **railroad** tracks, that they move on.

rain → **Rain** is the drops of water, called raindrops, that sometimes fall from clouds. **Rain** helps plants to grow, and keeps rivers and lakes full of water.

→ To **rain** means to **have raindrops falling.**
It is **raining. Raindrops are falling.** It also **rained** yesterday.

rainbow → The **rainbow** is the colors you sometimes see when the sun shines through raindrops.

raise → To **raise** means to **put** a thing **in a higher place.**
Can you **raise** the window?
Can you **put** it **in a higher place?** Can you **move** the window **up?**

→ To **raise** also means to **help** things **to grow.**
Some farmers **raise** fruit.
Some farmers **help** fruit **to grow.**

rather → I'd **rather** have the purple lollipop than the yellow one. I like the purple lollipop more.

151

reach

reach   ▶ To **reach** means to **stretch out and touch** something.
Can you **reach** the highest shelf?
Can you **stretch out and touch** it?

read   ▶ To **read** means to be able to **look at words and tell what they mean.**
Wilma can **read**. Wilma can **look at words and tell what they mean.**

ready   ▶ **Ready** means **having all the things you need** to do something.
Dinner is **ready.** The table is set and the food is cooked. We **have all the things we need** to eat dinner. We are **ready** to eat.

receive   ▶ To **receive** means to **get** something.
I **received** a letter from Grandma.
I **got** a letter from Grandma. Grandma sent a letter to me.

red   ▶ **Red** is a color. This is **red**.
Here is a **red** heart.

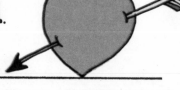

remember   ▶ To **remember** means to **not forget** something, or to **keep** it **in mind.**
I **remember** your birthday.
I **do not forget** your birthday. I know when your birthday comes. I **keep** it **in mind.**

repeat

To **repeat** means to **do or say** something **more than once.**

Can you **repeat** the answer?
Can you **say** the answer **one more time?**
Can you **say** the answer **again?**

---

reply

A **reply** is an **answer.**
What is your **reply?** What is your **answer?**

To **reply** means to **answer a question.**
"What game do you want to play?" I asked.
Jim **replied,** "Let's play Catch."
Jim **answered,** "Let's play Catch."

---

rest

The **rest** means **all the others.**
I have only one crayon. Where are the **rest** of the crayons? Where are **all the others?**

To **rest** means to **not do anything after being busy.**
I have been working all day. Now I will **rest.**
Now I will not do any work.

---

return

To **return** means to **go back,** or to **make something go back** to a place.
I **returned** the book to the library.
I **took** the book **back** to the library.

---

ribbon

A **ribbon** is a thin piece of cloth. **Ribbons** are made in many beautiful colors.

ride

ride To **ride** means to **be carried** by something.
I like **riding** in the car.
I like **being carried** by the car. I like sitting in the car and going to many places.

A leaf can **ride** the wind.
A leaf can **be carried** by the wind.

---

right **Right** means the **opposite of wrong.**
Two and two make? **2 4 6**
Which answer is **right?**
Which answer is **not wrong?**

Right also means the **opposite of left.**
Abby has a red mitten on her **right** hand. The red mitten is **not** on her **left** hand.
Walt's dog is sitting on his **right** side.

---

ring A **ring** is anything **shaped like a circle.**
Here is a key **ring.**
Here is a **ring** to wear on your finger.

To **ring** means to **go around** something.
Dotty's bracelet **rings** her wrist.
Dotty's bracelet **goes around** her wrist.
Dotty's bracelet **circles** her wrist.

Ring is also the **sound that a bell makes.**
A doorbell **rings.** Jingle bells **ring.**

154

river
A **river** is a large amount of water that is always moving, or flowing, to the ocean. Fish and other kinds of animals live in **rivers.** People can swim in **rivers.** To cross a **river,** people use boats or bridges.

road
A **road** is the ground that you move on, or the way, to a place. People drive cars, trucks, buses, and bicycles on **roads. A road** is also called a **highway.**

rob
To **rob** means to **steal,** or to **take things that belong to others.**
No one should **rob.** No one should **steal.**
No one should **take things that belong to others.**

rock
A **rock** is a very hard piece of the earth. **Rocks** come in many colors and shapes. **Rocks** may be large or small. **Rock** is also called **stone.**

roll
To **roll** means to turn over and over.
When a wheel moves, it **rolls.**
When a wheel moves, it **turns over and over.**

Marjorie **rolled** the clay into a ball.
Marjorie **turned** the clay **over and over** to shape it into a ball.

roller skate ➤ A **roller skate** is a plaything with four small wheels which fits on the bottom of your shoe. **Roller skates** are usually made of metal.

➤ To **roller-skate** means to **move on roller skates**.
Jenny is **roller-skating**.
Jenny is **moving on** her **roller skates**.

roof ➤ A **roof** is the **outside covering of the top of a building.**

room ➤ A **room** is an **inside part of a building.**
Teddy's house has six **rooms**.
Teddy's house has six **inside parts**. One **room** is the kitchen. There are also a living **room**, dining **room**, bathroom, and two bedrooms.

➤ **Room** means a **place**, or **space**, to put something.
Is there **room** on the shelf for another book?
Is there a **place** on the shelf for another book?
Is there **space** on the shelf for another book?

rope ➤ A **rope** is used to tie things. **Ropes** are made by twisting together pieces of wire or very strong string.

rose

A **rose** is a kind of flower that grows on a bush. **Roses** come in many colors. The stems of **roses** have sharp, pointy thorns that can hurt your fingers.

---

rough

Rough means **uneven** or **bumpy**.
We drove on a **rough** road.
We drove on an **uneven** and **bumpy** road.

---

round

Round is a shape. A wheel and a dime are **round**. Most balls are **round**. Can you name some other things that are **round?**

row

A **row** is a number of persons or things placed next to one another in a line.
In school, the students sit in **rows.**
In school, the students sit next to one another in a line.

Our garden has a **row** of daffodils. The daffodils grow next to one another in lines.

To **row** means to **use oars to make a boat move.**
Dad let me **row** the boat.
Dad let me **use** the **oars to make the boat move.**

rug

rug

➥ A **rug** is a thick, flat covering for a part of a floor.

---

ruler

➥ A **ruler** is a tool used to measure things and to help people draw straight lines. **Rulers** have smooth edges and are made of wood, metal, or plastic.

run

➥ To **run** means to use your legs to move faster than when you walk or hop or skip.
    I **ran** to school today.
    I moved faster than when I walk, hop, or skip.

➥ Please **run** to the store for me.
    Please **make a quick trip** to the store for me.

➥ A bicycle **runs** on its wheels.
    A bicycle **moves** on its wheels.

➥ Is the clock **running?**
    Is the clock **going?** Is it **working?**

➥ Which road **runs** to the beach?
    Which road **leads** to the beach?
    Which road **goes** to the beach?

---

rush

➥ To **rush** means to **hurry to do** something.
    I **rushed** to wash for dinner.
    I **hurried** to wash for dinner. I did not want to be late, so I quickly washed.

Ss

sad

Sad means **not happy.**
Wendy is **sad** because her toy is broken.
Wendy is **not happy.**

---

sail

A **sail** is a large piece of cloth used to make some boats move. Wind blows into the **sail** and makes the boat move across water.

To **sail** means to **move across water** using a boat or a ship.
Have you ever been **sailing?**
Have you ever **moved across water** on a boat or a ship?

---

same

Same means **alike.**
These bugs look the **same.** They look **alike.**

Same also means **equal.**

$$2 + 2 = 4 \qquad 6 - 2 = 4$$

The answers are the **same.** They are **equal.**

sand ➡Sand is very tiny pieces of rock. A beach is made of sand.

---

sandwich ➡A sandwich is two pieces of bread with some kind of food between them.

---

saucer ➡A saucer is a small dish.
Here are a cup and a saucer.

---

save ➡To save means to keep someone from being hurt.
At the beach, lifeguards save people.
They keep people from being hurt.

➡To save means to not use a thing now.
Ron is saving his money.
Ron is not using his money now. He is putting it in his piggy bank. Later, maybe he will spend the money he has saved.

---

saw ➡A saw is a tool used to cut wood, metal, and other things. Saws have many sharp points, called teeth, that do the cutting.

➡To saw means to use a saw to cut a thing.
We sawed wood for a fire.
We used a saw to cut wood for a fire.

---

say ➡To say means to make words into sounds.
Liza said, "How do I say the word spelled b-i-c-y-c-l-e? How do I make the word into a sound?"

scarf  → A **scarf** is used to keep your neck warm. **Scarves** are made of cloth or yarn.

school → **School** is a place where you go to learn things. In some **schools,** you can learn about numbers, and to read and write. In other **schools,** you can learn to draw, swim, or do many other things.

scissors  → A **scissors** is a tool used to cut paper and cloth and other things. **Scissors** have two sharp edges, called blades, that cut when they move past each other.

sea → The **sea** is the water that covers most of the earth. **Sea** water tastes salty. A **sea** is also called an **ocean.**

seat → A **seat** is a **place to sit.** A chair and a bench are **seats.** A bus has many **seats.** A bicycle has one **seat.**

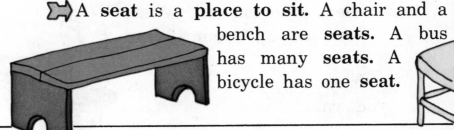

secret → A **secret** is **something known by very few people.**
I know a **secret.**
I know **something known by very few people.**

→ **Secret** means **unknown.**
Dad's present is in a **secret** place.
Dad's present is in an **unknown** place.

see

To **see** means to **use your eyes to know** things.
I **see** a bird in the tree.
I **use my eyes to know** there is a bird in the tree. I have **seen** birds in the tree many times. I **saw** one yesterday.

To **see** also means to **visit** someone.
I'm going to **see** my aunt. I'm going to **visit** her.

---

seed

A **seed** is the part of a plant that can grow into a new plant.

---

seem

It **seems** the snow is turning to rain.
It **appears** the snow is turning to rain.
It **looks as if** the snow is turning to rain.

---

seesaw

A **seesaw** is a plaything you and your friend can sit on. When you go up, your friend goes down. When your friend goes up, you go down.

---

send

To **send** means to **mail** letters and packages.
Davey **sent** a postcard to me.
Davey **mailed** a postcard to me.

---

seven

Seven is a number. It is also written as **7.** Can you count the **seven** olives?

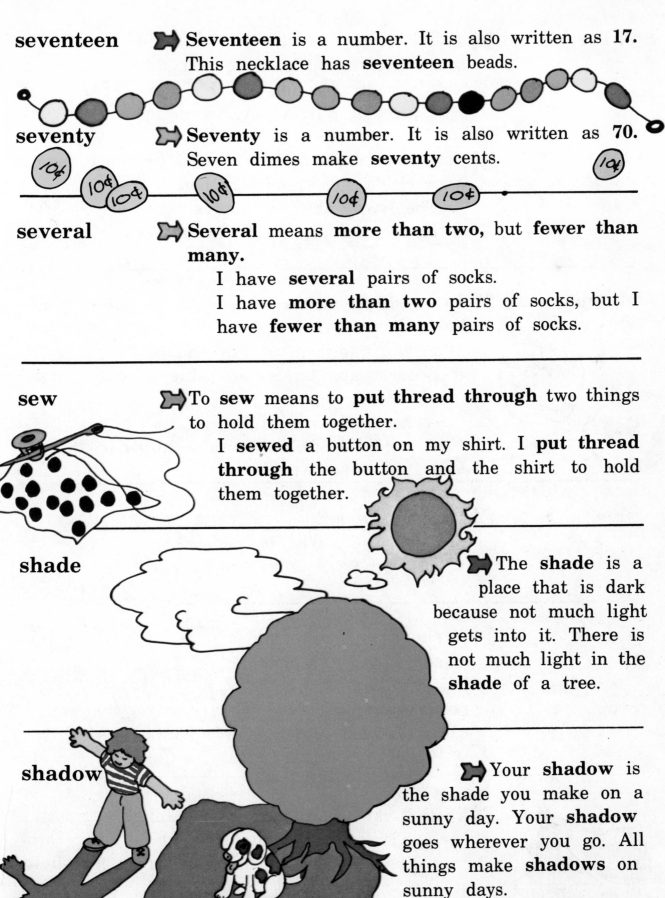

seventeen ➤ **Seventeen** is a number. It is also written as **17**. This necklace has **seventeen** beads.

seventy ➤ **Seventy** is a number. It is also written as **70**. Seven dimes make **seventy** cents.

several ➤ **Several** means **more than two,** but **fewer than many.**

I have **several** pairs of socks.
I have **more than two** pairs of socks, but I have **fewer than many** pairs of socks.

sew ➤ To **sew** means to **put thread through** two things to hold them together.

I **sewed** a button on my shirt. I **put thread through** the button and the shirt to hold them together.

shade ➤ The **shade** is a place that is dark because not much light gets into it. There is not much light in the **shade** of a tree.

shadow ➤ Your **shadow** is the shade you make on a sunny day. Your **shadow** goes wherever you go. All things make **shadows** on sunny days.

163

share

share → To **share** means to **give** someone **a part** of something that belongs to you.

I **shared** my lunch with Petey.
I **gave a part** of my lunch to Petey.

→ To **share** also means that **two or more people own** or do something together.

The **two** brothers **share** one bicycle. The bicycle **belongs to both** brothers.

sharp → To be **sharp** means to be **able to cut or make holes** in things.

Scissors and knives are **sharp.**
Scissors and knives are **able to cut** things.

A needle is **sharp.**
A needle is **able to make holes** in things.

she → Marion is a girl.

She is a girl. Who is Marion?

She is my older sister.

sheep → A **sheep** is an animal. **Sheep** have very thick hair called wool. A young **sheep** is called a lamb.

shell → A **shell** is a hard covering. A bird's egg has a **shell.** Turtles and snails have **shells** they carry on their backs. Have you ever looked for **shells** at the seashore?

should

shine   To **shine** means to **give out light.**
The sun **shines.** The sun **gives out light.**

ship   A **ship** is a **large boat.**

shirt   A **shirt** is a kind of clothes. **Shirts** cover your body from your neck to your waist.

shoe   A **shoe** is a hard covering for your foot. There are many kinds of **shoes.**

short   **Short** means **not tall.**
Tulips are **short** plants.
Tulips are **not tall.** Violets are **shorter.**
They are not as tall as tulips. Buttercups are the **shortest** of the three.

   Short also means **not long.**
Some shirts have **short** sleeves. Some shirts have sleeves that are **not long.**

should   You **should** take an umbrella today.
You **ought** to take an umbrella. It might rain.

   I **should** finish my homework soon.
I **ought** to finish soon. It is almost bedtime.

shout

shout ➡️To **shout** means to **speak in a loud voice.** Everyone at the football game **shouted.** They **spoke in loud voices.**

➡️A **shout** is a **yell.** I heard a **shout** for help. I heard a **yell** for help. I heard a **cry** for help.

---

shovel ➡️A **shovel** is a tool used for digging, and for lifting and throwing soil and other things. Do you have a **shovel** to use at the beach?

➡️To **shovel** means to use a shovel. We **shoveled** the snow from the sidewalk. We **used a shovel** to lift the snow and throw it from the sidewalk.

---

show ➡️To **show** means to **let** something **be seen.** **Show** me your new tooth. **Let** me **see** your new tooth.

---

shut ➡️To **shut** means to **close** something. When I go to sleep, I **shut** my eyes. When I go to sleep, I **close** my eyes.

➡️**Shut** means **closed,** or **not open.** The window is **shut.** The window is **closed.** It is **not open.** No breeze is coming in the window.

sick ➡ To be **sick** means to be **ill**, or **not well**.
Mother is **sick**. She is **ill**. She is **not well** because she has a cold.

---

side ➡ This clown's clothes are yellow on his left **side** and green on his right **side**.

➡ There is a dot on either **side** of the line.

➡ A penny has a picture on either **side**.

➡ A square has four **sides**.

➡ Suzie sleeps with her doll by her **side**. Her doll is next to her.

---

sidewalk ➡ A **sidewalk** is the ground people walk on next to a street or road.

---

sign ➡ A smile is a **sign** that tells you are happy.

➡ This picture is a **sign** that tells where to cross the street.

➡ A **sign** is written words that tell something.

➡ To **sign** means to **write your name.**
Jenny **signed** her name. Jenny **wrote** *Jenny.*

silent

silent ⟹ To be **silent** means to **not make sounds.**
Please be **silent.**
Please do **not make sounds.**

---

since ⟹ We have been on vacation **since** last week. Our vacation began last week.

I have gone to school **since** I was five years old. I have gone to school **from the time** I was five years old. I still go to school.

⟹ **Since** it is cold, I will wear gloves.
Because it is cold, I will wear gloves.

---

sing ⟹ To **sing** means to **use your voice to make music.**
We hear people **singing. They are using their voices to make music.**

---

sink ⟹ To **sink** means to **not stay on top** of a liquid.
A rock **sinks** in water.
A rock **does not stay on top** of water.

⟹ A **sink** is a container that holds water for washing. **Sinks** have places in their bottoms, called drains, to let the dirty water out. In the kitchen **sink,** you wash dishes, pots, and pans. In the bathroom sink, you wash your hands and face.

---

sister ⟹ Your **sister** is a girl or a woman who has the same mother and father as you. Do you have a **sister?** Is she older or younger than you?

168

sit ➡ To **sit** means to place the lower part of your body on a chair or other thing.
Pam is **sitting** on her favorite chair.
I **sat** on a tree stump.
Our cat likes to **sit** on the window sill.

six ➡ **Six** is a number. It is also written as **6.** Here are **six** mittens.

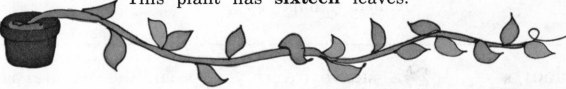

sixteen ➡ **Sixteen** is a number. It is also written as **16.** This plant has **sixteen** leaves.

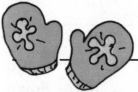

sixty ➡ **Sixty** is a number. It is also written as **60.** Six dimes make **sixty** cents.

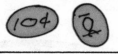

size ➡ **Size** means **how big** something is.
What **size** is an ant?
How big is an ant? Its **size** is small.

skin ➡ **Skin** is the smooth covering on all of your body. People have different **skin** colors.

skirt  ➡ A **skirt** is a loose covering for a girl or woman's body from the waist down. **Skirts** cover part or all of the legs.

sky

sky

The **sky** is the outdoors far above our heads. In the daytime, the **sky** is light. If there are no clouds in the **sky**, we can see the sun. In the nighttime, the **sky** is dark. When there are no clouds in the nighttime **sky,** we can see stars and sometimes the moon.

sleep

Sleep is the rest your body needs to grow and stay healthy. When you go to **sleep,** you lie down and close your eyes. A short amount of **sleep** is called a nap.

sleeve

A **sleeve** covers your arm. **Sleeves** are parts of coats, sweaters, and other clothes.

slice

A **slice** is a flat, thin piece that has been cut from something larger.
Here are some **slices** of watermelon.
Here are some flat, thin pieces that have been cut from the watermelon.

To **slice** means to **cut** something **into slices.**
The pizza has been **sliced.**
The pizza has been **cut into slices.**

slide

To **slide** means to **move smoothly** along the top of something.

> I can **slide** on ice.
> I can **move smoothly** on top of ice.

A **slide** is a kind of plaything that is very smooth. You climb to the top of a **slide,** sit down, and move smoothly down it.

---

slipper

A **slipper** is a soft, warm covering for your foot. When you get ready for bed, do you put on a pair of **slippers?**

---

slow

Slow means **not fast.**

> A turtle is **slow** when it moves.
> A turtle is **not fast** when it moves. It takes a turtle a long time to move from one place to another.

---

smell

To **smell** means to use your nose to know something you cannot see, taste, touch, or hear. Your nose can tell you what is pleasing, or not pleasing, to you. The **smell** of cookies baking in an oven is good. The **smell** of food that is old, or rotten, is bad.

smile

    smile   ⇒ To **smile** means to **make a happy face** by turning up the corners of your mouth.
Peggy is **smiling.**

---

    smooth   ⇒ **Smooth** means **not bumpy.**
A mirror is **smooth.** It is **not bumpy.**

---

    snail   ⇒ A **snail** is a small animal that lives inside a shell. **Snails** live in water or on land.

---

    snake   ⇒ A **snake** is a long, thin animal. **Snakes** have no legs, but they can move very fast.

    snow   ⇒ **Snow** is very small, white pieces of icy water that fall from clouds when it is very cold. A piece of **snow** is called a snowflake. Snowflakes come in many beautiful shapes.

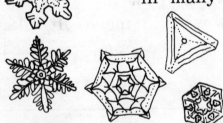

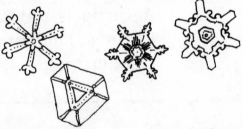

    so   ⇒ Joe is a boy. **So** am I. I am a boy **also.**

         ⇒ A giant is **so** tall! A giant is **very** tall!

         ⇒ Is that **so?** Is that **true?**

         ⇒ I have fifteen pennies or **so.** I have **about** fifteen pennies.

sock

A **sock** is a soft covering for your foot and a part of your leg. **Socks** are worn under your shoes.

---

soft

Soft means **not hard.**

A pillow is **soft.** It is **not hard.** You can change the shape of a pillow.

---

soil

Soil is the brown, red, or black soft part of the earth that plants grow in. Some animals make their homes in **soil.**

---

some

Some people have yellow hair.

A number of people have yellow hair. Other people do not.

---

son

A **son** is the boy child of his father and mother. A man is the **son** of his mother and father also. Mike is a boy. Mike is the **son** of his father and mother. Mike's father is the **son** of Mike's grandparents.

---

song

A **song** is **music and words** together. "Mary Had a Little Lamb" is a **song.** It is **words and music** together. Do you know the words? Do you know the music?

soon

soon ➡ We will be leaving **soon.**
We will be leaving **in a short time.**

---

sorry ➡ "I'm **sorry** I broke Ann's toy today," said Bobby. "I didn't mean to do it. I know it isn't kind to break other people's toys."

---

sound ➡ A **sound** is what we use our ears to know, or hear. When you talk, you make **sounds.** When you clap, you make a **sound.** A piano makes **sounds** when you play it. When a balloon breaks, it makes the **sound** BANG!

---

soup ➡ **Soup** is a hot or cold liquid food. **Soups** are made from water or milk, and may have meat, vegetables, or other foods in them. Do you like to eat **soup** for lunch? What kind of **soup** do you like best?

---

speak ➡ To **speak** means to **say words,** or to **talk.**
Who is **speaking?**
Who is **saying words?**
Who is **talking?**

---

special ➡ **Special** means **not usual.**
Your birthday is a **special** day.
Your birthday is **not** a **usual** day. It is not like the other days in a year.

174

spell

➡️ To **spell** means to **say or write the letters in a word in the right order.**
Can you **spell** "apple"?
Can you **say** or **write** a-p-p-l-e?

---

spend

➡️ To **spend** means to **use.**
How much money did you **spend?**
How much money did you **use?**

We **spent** all of our time playing.
We **used** all of our time playing.

---

spider

➡️ A **spider** is an insect that has eight legs.

---

spoon

A **spoon** is used for eating. **Spoons** have a handle, and a small bowl that can hold soup, cereal, and other things.

---

spread

➡️ To **spread** means to **make** something **lie flat.**
I **spread** butter on my bread. I **made** butter **lie flat** on top of it.

➡️ To **spread** means to **make** things **move apart.**
I **spread** my toes. I **made** them **move apart.**

---

spring

➡️ **Spring** is one of the four seasons of the year. **Spring** is the time between the cold winter and the warm summer. In the **spring** many plants have flowers. Many animals have their babies in the **spring.**

square

square ➤ A **square** is a shape that has four sides. All four sides of a **square** are the same size.

squeeze ➤ To **squeeze** means to **push in the sides.**
When you **squeeze** an orange, you get juice.
When you **push in the sides** of an orange, you get juice.

➤ To **squeeze** means to **try to fit** into a place.
We all **squeezed** into the car.
We all **tried to fit** into the car.

squirrel ➤ A **squirrel** is a small, furry animal. **Squirrels** have long tails and sharp little teeth.

stair ➤ A **stair** is a step you walk up to get to a higher place. You can also walk down **stairs** to get to a lower place. In some houses, you climb **stairs** to get to another floor.

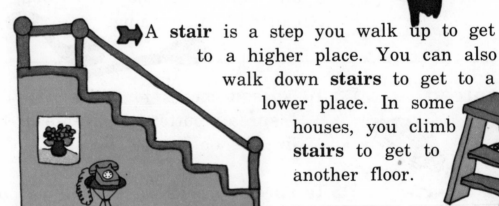

stand ➤ To **stand** means to be straight and tall with your feet on the ground.
When I **stand,** my feet are on the ground and my body is straight and tall. I am **standing** now. Today, I **stood** in front of the class to tell a story.

star

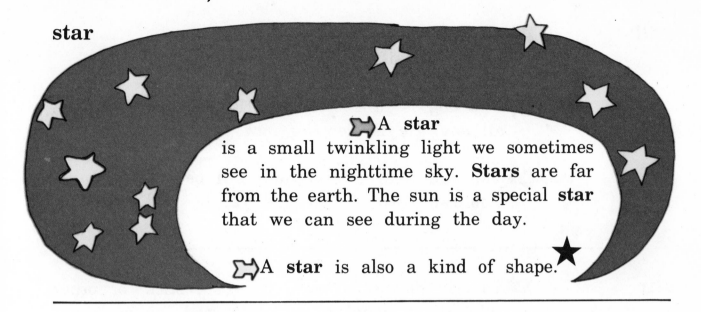

A **star** is a small twinkling light we sometimes see in the nighttime sky. **Stars** are far from the earth. The sun is a special **star** that we can see during the day.

A **star** is also a kind of shape.

stay

Marilyn told her dog, **"Stay."**
Marilyn told her dog, **"Don't go away."**

steal

To **steal** means to **take things that belong to other people.**
Who **stole** my cookies?
Who **took** my cookies?

step

A **step** is a place to put each foot when walking up or down something.
Stairs have **steps.** They have places to put your feet when walking up or down them.

stick

A **stick** is a long, thin piece of something, such as wood or chewing gum.

177

story   A **story** tells how something happened. **Stories** can be told in words only, or in pictures only, or in both words and pictures. A **story** is also called a **tale**.

straight   **Straight** means **not crooked or bent.**
This is a **straight** line.
This line is **not crooked or bent.**

stranger   A **stranger** is **someone you do not know.**

strawberry   A **strawberry** is a small, red fruit.

street   A **street** is a road in a city or town. Cars, buses, and trucks move on **streets.** On the sides of **streets** are sidewalks and buildings.

STORE

stretch   To **stretch** means to make something as big or as long as it can be.
When you **stretch** a rubber band, you pull it to make it as long as it can be.

strike   To **strike** means to touch something very hard. I used a hammer to **strike** the nail. I **hit** the nail. I touched the nail very hard.

string

string

➡️ **String** is used to tie things. **String** is made from long pieces of thread, which are twisted together.

stripe

➡️ A **stripe** is a **line of color.** Can you name these things that have **stripes?**

strong

➡️ **Strong** means **not weak.**
A **strong** person can lift heavy things.
A **strong** person is **not weak.**
A **strong** light is very bright.
A **strong** sound is very loud.

---

subtract

➡️ To **subtract** means to **take away from.**
Subtract six from eight to get two.
Take away six from eight to get two.

Using numerals, we write this as $8-6=2$
The sign − tells you to **subtract.** it is also called a **minus** sign.

---

sugar

➡️ **Sugar** is a very sweet food that comes from certain plants. **Sugar** is used to make candy, cake, and other things that taste sweet.

suit

A **suit** is a jacket and a pair of pants or a skirt that are worn together.

A bathing **suit** is the special clothes you wear to go swimming.

summer

Summer is one of the four seasons of the year. **Summer** is the warmest time.

sun

The **sun** is the yellow, white, or orange ball we see in the daytime sky. When the **sun** shines, it makes light and heat.

supper

Supper is the last meal of the day. Most people eat **supper** in the evening.

suppose

I **suppose** you are right.
I **guess** you are right, but I'm not sure.
I **think** you are right, but I'm not sure.

Supposing the mittens are lost?
What if the mittens are lost?

Kenny was **supposed** to do that work.
Kenny **should have** done that work.

sure

I'm **sure** of the answer.
I **know** the answer. I'm **certain** of it.

181

surprise

A **surprise** is something you don't know about. My birthday party was a **surprise.** I didn't know I was going to have a birthday party. It was a good **surprise.**

---

swallow

To **swallow** means to have food move down your throat to your stomach.

I **swallowed** my milk. It moved down my throat to my stomach.

---

swan

A **swan** is a large, white bird. **Swans** have long necks. They are very good swimmers.

---

sweater

A **sweater** is a kind of clothes used to cover your body from your neck to your waist. **Sweaters** are made of yarn.

swim

To **swim** means to use your arms and legs to move through water.

Bernice likes **swimming** in the ocean. Yesterday, she **swam** all day. She has **swum** every day this week.

---

swing

A **swing** is a plaything you can make move back and forth.

We have a **swing.** We can make it move back and forth.

table

A **table** is a kind of furniture. A **table** has a flat top and three or more legs. People sit at **tables** to eat, write, and do other things. People also put lamps and other things on tables.

tail

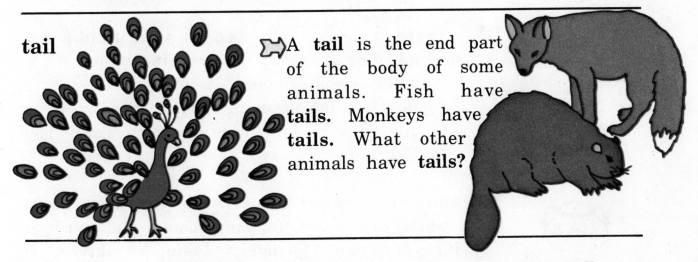

A **tail** is the end part of the body of some animals. Fish have **tails.** Monkeys have **tails.** What other animals have **tails?**

take

To use a hammer, you **take** it by its handle.
To use a hammer, you **hold** it by its handle.

Which lollipop did you **take?** Which one did you **pick?** Which one did you **choose?**

I **took** my books to school.
I **carried** my books to school.

We **took** the train to the beach. We used the train to go to the beach.

talk

talk ➤ To **talk** means to **say words.**
My baby sister is learning to **talk.**
My baby sister is learning to **say words.** She is learning to **speak.**

tall ➤ **Tall** means **how far** it is **from** the top of something **to** its **bottom.**
An ostrich is a **tall** bird. It is **far from** the **top** of an ostrich **to** its **bottom.**
An ostrich is **not short.**

taste ➤ To **taste** means to put food in your mouth and use your tongue to learn something about it.
I **tasted** some lemon.
I put some lemon in my mouth and used my tongue to learn something about it. The lemon **tasted** sour.

➤ The **taste** of something is what you learn about it when you put it in your mouth and touch it with your tongue. Sugar's **taste,** or **flavor,** is sweet. A lemon's **taste** is sour.

➤ A **taste** is a small amount of a food or a drink.
I will have a **taste** of the pie.
I will have a small amount of the pie.

teach ➤ To **teach** means to **help** someone **to learn.**
Roddy is **teaching** his brother to read.
Roddy is **helping** his brother **to learn** how to read.

184

teacher ⇒ A **teacher** is someone who helps people to learn. Who is your favorite **teacher** in school? What is your **teacher's** name? What does your **teacher** help you to learn?

---

team ⇒ A **team** is two or more people or animals that do something together.

My friends and I play on a baseball **team.** We play baseball together.

A **team** of horses can pull a wagon. Two or more horses working together can pull a wagon.

---

tear ⇒ A **tear** is a drop of water that falls from your eye when you cry. **Tears** are salty.

⇒ To **tear** means to have your eyes make the salty drops of water called tears.
The wind is causing my eyes to **tear.**
The wind is causing my eyes to make tears.

⇒ A **tear** is the place where something has been pulled apart.
There is a **tear** in my shirt. The tear is the place where the cloth of the shirt was pulled apart.

⇒ To **tear** also means to **pull** something **apart.**
Our cat likes to **tear** paper.
Our cat likes to **pull** paper **apart.** It **tore** the newspaper. Now the newspaper is **torn.**

telephone

telephone

A **telephone** is used to talk to and listen to people who are far away. The voices of people, and other sounds, move through **telephone** wires. A **telephone** is also called a **phone.**

To **telephone** means to **use a telephone** to talk to someone.
Who **telephoned** you? Who **called** you?
Who **used the telephone** to talk to you?

television

A **television** can send and receive pictures and sounds. **TV** is a short name for **television.**

tell

Can you **tell** how many nails there are?
Can you **count** how many nails there are?

Bob is **telling** us about his trip. Bob is using words to let us know what his trip was like.

I **told** you to be careful. I **said** that you should be careful.

ten

Ten is a number. **Ten** is also written as **10.** Here are **ten** bunnies.

tent

A **tent** is a kind of house that is made of cloth. When people go camping, they sometimes sleep in a **tent. Tents** are made in many shapes and sizes.

than

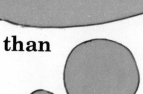

The green ball is bigger **than** the orange ball. The green ball is the bigger of the two balls. The orange ball is smaller **than** the green ball.

thank

To **thank** means to do or say something polite to a person who has done something for you.
Annie **thanked** her friend for the gift.
Annie said "**Thank** you" to her friend.

that

Sandy pointed to the pink cupcake and said, "I want **that** cupcake. **That** cupcake is the one I want."

their

Darin and Becky have a dog. The dog is **theirs.** The dog belongs to them. The name of **their** dog is Sparky.

them

I have a surprise for Mom and Dad.
I have a surprise for **them.**

then

then

⮕ First put on your jacket. **Then** you may go outdoors. You may go outdoors after you put on your jacket.

⮕ We will leave at six o'clock.
We will leave **then**. We will leave **at that time.**

---

there

⮕ Selma pointed to the park and said, "Let's play **there.** Let's play **in that place.**"

⮕ "I'm going to the library," I said. Larry said, "I'm also going **there.** May I go **there** with you?"

---

these

⮕ **These** socks have red stripes.

These socks have green stripes.

---

they

⮕ Ray and Michael are friends.
They are friends.
They're friends.

---

thick

⮕ **Thick** means **not thin.**
Here is a **thick** line. It is **not thin.**

A tree trunk is **thick.** It is **not thin.**
It is a long way around a tree trunk.

Honey is a **thick** liquid. It is **not thin.**
It is not easy to pour honey.

thin

➡ **Thin** means **not thick.**
Here is a **thin** line. It is **not thick.**

A hair is **thin.** It is **not thick.** It is not very big around.

Water is a **thin** liquid. It is **not thick.** It is easy to pour water.

---

thing

➡ What is this **thing** called?
What is this **object** called? What is it?

➡ I keep all my **things** in my room. I keep my clothes, toys, books, and all that I own in my room.

➡ I have many **things** to do before I go to school in the morning. I have to wash, get dressed, make my bed, and eat breakfast.

---

thirsty

➡ To be **thirsty** means to **need to drink.**
"I'm **thirsty**," said Fran.
"I **need to drink**," said Fran. "May I have some water?"

---

thirteen

➡ **Thirteen** is a number. It is also written as **13.** This flag has **thirteen** stripes.

thirty  **Thirty** is a number. **Thirty** is also written as **30.** Three dimes make **thirty** cents.

this Timothy showed his friend a cup and said, "**This** is my cup. **This** cup has my name on it."

those Betty looked at her friend's new shoes and said, "Are **those** shoes new? I have never seen **those** before."

though **Though** it may rain, we are going picnicking. **Even if** it rains, we are going picnicking.

Though the cake looks good, I don't want any. The cake looks good, yet I don't want any.

thread A **thread** is a long, thin piece of cotton, wool, plastic, or other thing. **Thread** is used to sew. Cloth is made of many **threads.**

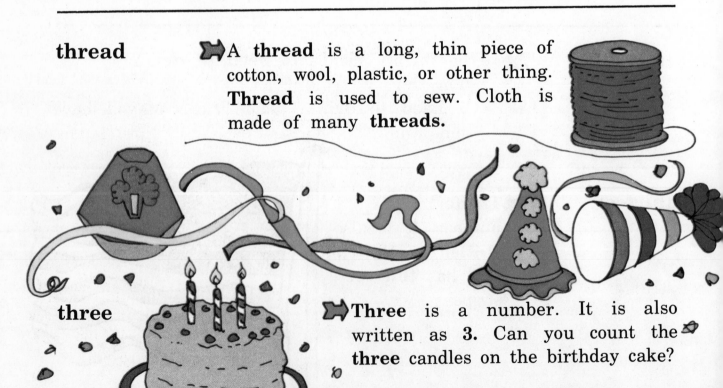

three **Three** is a number. It is also written as **3.** Can you count the **three** candles on the birthday cake?

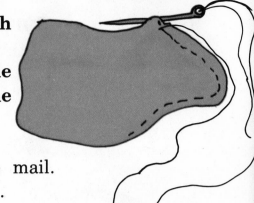

through   ➡A needle can go **through** cloth.
A needle can go **in one side** of cloth **and** come **out the other** side.

➡I sent a letter **through** the mail.
I sent a letter **by** the mail.

➡Birds fly **through** the air.
Birds fly **in** the air.

➡Are you **through** with your schoolwork?
Are you **finished** with your schoolwork?

➡The baby slept **through** the night.
The baby slept **during** the night.

---

throw   ➡To **throw** means to use your hand and your arm to make something move through the air.
Jamie **threw** the baseball. He used his hand and arm to make the baseball move through the air.

---

thumb   ➡Your **thumb** is a finger that is short, thick, and very strong. You have two **thumbs,** one on each hand. You use your **thumb** and one or more other fingers to pick up and hold things.

---

tickle   ➡To **tickle** means to **touch** something **very lightly.**
When you tickled my foot, you **touched** it **very lightly.** It made me want to laugh.

tie

tie

To **tie** means to use a string, ribbon, or other thing to **make a knot.**
> I **tied** the red ribbon.
> I **made a knot** in the red ribbon.

A **tie** is anything that you can use to make a knot. A rope and a shoelace are kinds of **ties.**

A **tie** is also a kind of clothes. A **tie** is a long, thin piece of cloth that is worn around a person's neck. Here are some **ties.**

tiger

A **tiger** is a large, strong animal that has stripes. **Tigers** live in some jungles.

tight

I held my doll **tightly.** I held my doll **close.** I hugged my doll.

My shoes are too **tight** for my feet. My shoes are too small for my feet.

The bottle cap is **tight.**
The bottle cap is **not loose.**

till

It snowed **till** the morning.
It snowed **until** the morning.
It snowed **up to** the morning.

time

➡️ **Time** is how people measure how long things last. People have names for amounts of **time**. A minute, an hour, a day, and a year are amounts of **time**. People use clocks, watches, the sun, and the moon to measure, or tell, **time**.

➡️ To **tell time** means to look at a clock, the sun, or the moon, and say how much time of a day has passed.

"I can **tell time**," said Louisa. "If I look at the clock and see the big hand on the twelve and the small hand on the four, I know it is four o'clock."

tiny

➡️ **Tiny** means **very small**.

tip

➡️ The **tip** of something is its **end. Tips** are usually pointy. A pencil has two **tips**. One of the **tips** is pointy.

tiptoe

➡️ To **tiptoe** means to **walk on the tips,** or ends, **of your toes.**
Can you **tiptoe?**
Can you **walk on the tips of your toes?**

tire

➡️ A **tire** is a **wheel made of rubber.** Cars, bicycles, and other things have **tires.**

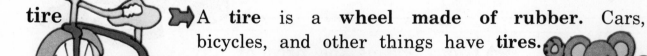

tired

tired ⇨ To be **tired** means to **need a rest.**
"It is late and I am **tired**," said Dad.
"I **need a rest.** I am going to sleep."

---

to ⇨ Brian threw the ball **to** me.
Brian threw the ball **toward** me. Brian threw the ball in my direction.

⇨ A glass is used **to** drink from. A glass is used for drinking.

⇨ The time is ten minutes **to** three.
The time is ten minutes **of** three.
The time is ten minutes **before** three.

⇨ We played from four **to** six o'clock.
We played from four **until** six o'clock. We played between four and six o'clock.

---

toast ⇨ **Toast** is bread that has been heated to make it turn brown. Do you like jelly on your **toast?**

⇨ To **toast** means to use heat to make something warm and brown.
I like to **toast** marshmallows.
I like to use the heat of a fire to make marshmallows warm and brown.

---

today ⇨ **Today** means the **present day.**
Is **today** your birthday?
Is the **present day** your birthday?
Is **this day** your birthday?

toe ⟹ Your **toe** is a part of your body. You have ten **toes,** five at the end of each foot.

⟹ Some animals have **toes.** Cats have **toes.** Fish do not have **toes.**

---

together ⟹ My friends and I go to school **together.**
My friends and I go to school **in a group.**

⟹ Can you jump with your feet **together?**
Can you jump with your feet **touching?**

⟹ Thunder and lightning can happen **together.**
Thunder and lightning can happen **at the same time.**

---

tomato ⟹ A **tomato** is a fruit. Most **tomatoes** are red. Inside a **tomato** are many little seeds.

---

tomorrow ⟹ **Tomorrow** is the **day after today.**
Our vacation begins **tomorrow.**
Our vacation begins the **day after today.**

---

tongue ⟹ Your **tongue** is a part of your body that is inside your mouth. You can move your **tongue.** You use your **tongue** to eat, taste, and talk.

---

tonight ⟹ **Tonight** is the **night part of today.**
We will not leave until **tonight.**
We will not leave until the **night part of today.** We will not leave until it is dark.

too   Sharon is a girl. Her sister is a girl **also.**
Her sister is a girl **too.**

tool   A **tool** is a thing people use to make work easier.
A saw is a **tool** used to cut wood. A saw makes the work of cutting wood easier.

A pencil is a writing **tool.** A pencil makes the work of writing easier.

tooth   Your **tooth** is a small, hard, white part of your body. Your **teeth** are inside your mouth. You need your **teeth** to eat and talk.

toothbrush   A **toothbrush** is a small brush used to keep your teeth clean and healthy.

top   The **top** of something is its **highest part.**
Your head is the **top** of your body.
Your head is the **highest part** of your body.

A **top** is a **cover, lid,** or **cap.**
Where is the bottle **top?**
Where is the **cover?** Where is the **cap?**
Where is the **lid** to the bottle?

touch   To **touch** means to put your hands or another part of your body against or on something.
To play a piano, you **touch** its keys. You put your fingers on the keys of the piano.

toward

When something falls, it moves **toward** the ground. It moves **in the direction of** the ground. It moves **to** the ground.

towel

A **towel** is a piece of paper or cloth. **Towels** are used to wipe and dry wet things.

town

A **town** is a place where many people live. There are stores, schools, and other buildings in **towns.** A **town** is not as big as a city. Do you live in a **town?** What is the name of your **town?**

toy

A **toy** is a thing you can play with. A doll and a ball are **toys.** You can play with a doll. You can play with a ball. What is your favorite **toy?**

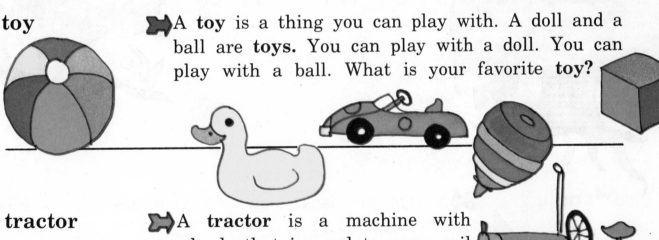

tractor

A **tractor** is a machine with wheels that is used to move soil and other things. Some farmers use **tractors.**

traffic

Traffic is the **moving cars, buses, and trucks** you see on streets and roads.

train

A **train** is a line of railroad cars.

travel

➡ To **travel** means to **go from one place to another.**

Cars **travel** on roads. Cars **move** on roads. Cars **go from one place to another** on roads.

➡ This vacation, we are **traveling** to the ocean. This vacation, we are **going to** the ocean. This vacation, we are **taking a trip** to the ocean.

tree

➡ A **tree** is a plant. **Trees** have leaves and make flowers and fruit. The hard part of **trees** is called wood. Oak, pine, and cherry are some kinds of **trees.** Can you name other kinds of trees?

triangle

➡ A **triangle** is a shape. A **triangle** always has three sides.

trip

➡ To **take a trip** means to **go to** a place, or to **visit** it.

We **took a trip** to a museum. We **went to** a museum. We **visited** a museum.

trousers

➡ **Trousers** is another name for **long pants.**

truck A **truck** is used to carry things. A dump **truck** is used to carry soil. A fire **truck** is used to carry water and tools for fighting fires. An ice-cream **truck** carries many kinds of ice-cream.

truth I asked Vinny, "Did you take my toy?" Vinny said, "Yes, I took your toy." Vinny told the **truth.** Vinny told what happened. Vinny did not lie.

try Mom is **trying** to open the window. Mom is working hard to open the window. The window seems to be stuck. If she **tries** hard enough, she will be able to open the window.

Jacqueline **tried** on her mother's hat. Jacqueline put on her mother's hat. She wanted to see if the hat would fit her.

Would you like to **try** the chocolate cake? Would you like to **taste** the chocolate cake?

tube A **tube** is a long, round, hollow shape. A straw is a **tube** made of paper or plastic.

tulip A **tulip** is a very pretty kind of flower. Here are some **tulips.**

tunnel

➤A **tunnel** is a large, round, hollow place for people to move through. Some **tunnels** are built under rivers or other bodies of water. People can drive through a **tunnel** to get to the other side of a river.

turkey

➤A **turkey** is a large bird. Do you have **turkey** for dinner on Thanksgiving Day?

turn

➤A moving wheel **turns** around and around.

➤I am **turning** the radio on. I am making the radio work so I can listen to it.

➤When you **turn** something over, you see its other side.

➤We watched the car **turn** the corner.
We watched the car **go around** the corner.

➤Henry **turned** his chair to the television.
Henry made his chair face the television.

➤In the fall, some leaves **turn** color.
In the fall, some leaves **change** color.

➤Some roads have many **turns**.
Some roads have many **bends**.
Some roads have many **curves**.

➤Is it my **turn** to sing?
Is it my **chance** to sing? May I sing now?

turtle

A **turtle** is an animal. **Turtles** carry a covering called a shell on their backs. Most **turtles** live on land and in water. Some **turtles** can live only on land.

---

twelve

Twelve is a number. It is also written as **12**. **Twelve** is also called a **dozen.** Here are **twelve** seashells.

twenty

Twenty is a number. **Twenty** is also written as **20.** Two dimes make **twenty** cents.

---

twice

Twice means **two times.**
I have read that book **twice.**
I have read that book **two times.**

---

twin

A **twin** is one of two people who have the same parents and were born on the same day. **Twins** may or may not look alike.

---

two

Two is a number. **Two** is also written as **2.** Here are **two** peaches.

---

typewriter

A **typewriter** is a machine that makes putting words on paper easier. A **typewriter** has a different spot to touch, called a key, for each letter of the alphabet.

Uu

umbrella   An **umbrella** is used to keep us dry in the rain and cool in the hot sun.

uncle   Your **uncle** is your father's, or your mother's, brother. An **uncle** is also the man who is married to your aunt.

under   We ate lunch **under** the tree.
We ate lunch **below** the tree.
We ate lunch **beneath** the tree.

understand   To **understand** means to **know how.**
Mary Lou **understands** how to subtract.
Mary Lou **knows how** to subtract.

unicorn   A **unicorn** is a make-believe animal. **Unicorns** look very much like horses. A long horn grows from a **unicorn's** head.

unless   We will have a picnic **unless** it rains.
We will have a picnic, **but not if** it rains.
We will have a picnic, **except if** it rains.

until   ➤Christopher played **until** bedtime.
Christopher played **up to** bedtime.

➤Vacation does not begin **until** tomorrow.
Vacation does not begin **before** tomorrow.

up   ➤**Up** means the **opposite of down.**
Julio climbed **up** the latter.
Julio climbed **from the bottom** of the
ladder **to the top** of the ladder.

We watched the balloon float **up.**
We watched it float **high** into the sky.

upon   ➤We sat **upon** the rug. We sat **on** the rug.

us   ➤Belinda is going to school with **us.**
Belinda is going to school with **you and me.** We
will go to school with Belinda.

use   ➤Do you know how to **use** a bicycle? To **use** a
bicycle, you ride on it.

➤I am **using** the ball. I am playing with it.

➤We **used** colored pencils to draw pictures. We
drew pictures with colored pencils.

usually    ➤Grass is **usually** green.
Grass is **almost always** green. Most grass is
green.

Vv

vacation

⇨**Vacation** is the time when people rest from working or from going to school. What do you do during your summer **vacation?**

valentine

⇨Your **valentine** is someone you like very much.

⇨A **valentine** is a card or letter you send to a person you like very much. Have you ever sent or received a **valentine?**

vase

⇨A **vase** is a container used to hold flowers.

vegetable

⇨A **vegetable** is a **plant,** or part of a plant, **we eat.** Peas, lettuce, carrots, onions, and potatoes are **vegetables.** Can you name some other **vegetables?**

very

⇨Our baby brother is **very** young. He is **so** young he cannot walk or talk yet.

village   ⇨A **village** is a small town. **Villages** have few people or buildings.

vine   ⇨A **vine** is a kind of plant that grows to be very long. **Vines** grow along the ground, or up trees, walls, and sides of buildings. Grapes, ivy, and morning glories are **vines.**

violet   ⇨A **violet** is a small flower that has white, blue, purple, or yellow flowers. **Violets** smell good.

violin   ⇨A **violin** is a musical instrument. To play a **violin,** you touch its strings.

visit   ⇨To **visit** means to **go to see** someone.
On Sunday, we **visited** Grandpa.
On Sunday, we **went to see** Grandpa.

⇨To **visit** also means to **go to a place.**
Let's **visit** the park this afternoon.
Let's **go to** the park this afternoon.

voice   ⇨Your **voice** is the sounds you make with your mouth and throat. You use your **voice** to talk, sing, laugh, and shout.

voyage   ⇨A **voyage** is a long trip. Ships make **voyages** across the ocean. Airplanes make **voyages** to places that are far away.

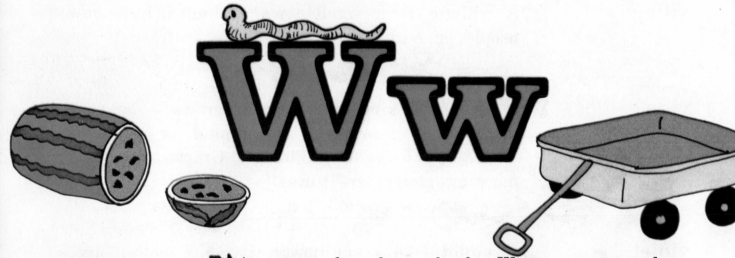

wagon   ➤A **wagon** has four wheels. **Wagons** are used to carry people and things. To make a **wagon** move, you pull it.

---

walk   ➤To walk means to **stand and use** your **legs to move slowly.**

The baby is learning to **walk.**

The baby is learning to **stand and use** her **legs to move slowly.** When older, she will learn to run, hop, skip, and jump.

---

want   ➤To **want** means you **would like to have** something.

I **want** a party on my birthday.

I **would like to have** a party on my birthday.

➤To **want** something also means to **need** it.

How much lunch money do you **want?**

How much lunch money do you **need?**

---

warm   ➤**Warm** means **not cool.**

Summer weather is **warm.**

Summer weather is **not cool.**

wash

➡️ To **wash** means to **use water** or another liquid, **and sometimes soap, to make** something **clean.** After lunch, we **washed** the dishes. We **used water and soap to make** the dishes **clean.**

---

watch

➡️ To **watch** means to **look at** something. Who is **watching** television? Who is **looking** at television?

➡️ To **watch for** something means to **look and wait for** it. I **watched for** the mail to come. I **looked and waited** for the mail to come.

➡️ A **watch** is a small clock. A pocket **watch** is carried in your pocket. A **watch** you wear on your wrist is called a wristwatch.

---

water

➡️ **Water** is a thin liquid that has no color. The seas, rivers, and **lakes** on the earth are made of **water.** Rain is **water.** All people, plants, and animals need **water.**

➡️ To **water** means to **put water on** something. Barbie is **watering** her garden. Barbie is **putting water on** her garden.

---

watermelon

➡️ A **watermelon** is a large fruit that grows on a vine. **Watermelons** have a hard, green outside part and a soft, pink or red inside part.

wave

➡A **wave** is a shape that goes up and down.
This line is a **wave.** ⌇⌇⌇⌇⌇
This line is a shape that goes up and down.

The ocean's **waves** go up and down.

➡To **wave** means to **move up and down or back
and forth.**
When you **wave** "Hello" or "Good-by," you
move your hand **back and forth.**

---

we

➡**We** is the word you use when talking or writing
about yourself and one or more other people.
Janie said, "Mona and I play together."
Janie said, "**We** play together."

---

weak

➡**Weak** means **not strong.**
A baby is **weak.** A baby is **not strong.** A
baby cannot lift heavy things.
A **weak** sound is not very loud.
A **weak** light is not very bright.

---

wear

➡To **wear** means to **have** something
on your body.
Are you **wearing** your hat? Do
you **have** your hat **on** your head?

Ted has **worn** a smile on his face
all day.
Ted has **had** a smile **on** his face all day.

weather   ➡ **Weather** is rain, snow, and wind. It is also hot days, cold days, sunny and cloudy days.

---

week   ➡ A **week** is an amount of time. A **week** is seven days long. The days of the **week** are Sunday, Monday, Tuesday, Wednesday, Thursday, Friday, and Saturday. Fifty-two **weeks** make a year.

---

weight   ➡ The **weight** of something is **how heavy** it is. What is the **weight** of a feather? **How heavy** is a feather? A feather has little **weight.**

---

well   ➡ Catherine is feeling **well** today.
Catherine is feeling **good** today.
Catherine is **not** feeling **sick** today.

➡ A **well** is a deep hole in the ground that is always full of water. Some farmers use the water from **wells** to help make plants grow.

---

wet   ➡ **Wet** means **not dry.**
The grass is **wet** from the rain.
The grass is **not dry.** The rain made the grass **wet.**

---

whale   ➡ A **whale** is an animal that lives in the sea. **Whales** can swim, but they are not fish. One kind of **whale** is the largest animal in the world.

what

what   ▶ **What** is your name? Tell me your name.

▶ **What** is your age? How old are you?

▶ **What** did you say? Please say it again.

---

wheel   ▶ A **wheel** is shaped like a circle. When a **wheel** moves, it turns around. **Wheels** make it easy to move things. A bicycle has two **wheels.** When you move a bicycle, the **wheels** turn around. Can you name some other things that have **wheels?**

---

when   ▶ **When** did Patricia leave for school? **At what time** did Patricia leave for school?

▶ You eat **when** you are hungry. You eat **at the time that** you are hungry.

---

where   ▶ **Where** are you going? **To what place** are you going?

▶ **Where** are your shoes? **In what place** are your shoes?

▶ Our dog likes to sleep **where** it is warm. Our dog likes to sleep **in a place** that is warm.

whether

➤ Do you know **whether** Charlie is at home?
Whether or not Charlie is at home, I am going to the party.

---

which

➤ **Which** toy do you want? There are many toys. You may choose one.

---

while

➤ Will you play with me for a **while?**
Will you play with me for a **short time?**

➤ You can read **while** I wash the dishes.
You can read **during the time that** I am washing the dishes.

➤ Can you rub your stomach **while** you pat your head? Can you do both things **at the same time?**

---

whisker

➤ A **whisker** is a long hair that grows from the face of some animals. A sea lion has **whiskers.**

➤ **Whiskers** is another name for a man's beard.

---

whisper

➤ A **whisper** is something said in a **soft voice.**
Please speak in a **whisper.**
Please speak in a **soft voice.**

➤ To **whisper** means to **speak in a soft voice.**
We **whispered** while we were in the library.
We **spoke in very soft voices.** We were not loud.

whistle

whistle   ➤A **whistle** is a musical instrument. To make a sound with a **whistle,** you blow into it. Some trains and boats have big **whistles.**

➤To **whistle** means to make a sharp, high sound. The teakettle is **whistling.**
The teakettle is making a sharp, high sound. It sounds like "phweeeeet."

white   ➤**White** is a color. This is **white.**
Snow is **white.**

who   ➤**Who** doesn't want ice cream?
What person doesn't want ice cream?
Which person doesn't want ice cream?

whole   ➤**Whole** means **all** of a thing.
I ate the **whole** pie.
I ate **all** of the pie.

➤**Whole** means **full.**
I have a **whole** box of crayons.
I have a **full** box of crayons.

➤**Whole** also means **unbroken.**
My toy is **whole.** My toy is **unbroken.**

whom   ➤For **whom** is this letter?
For **what person** is this letter?

whose   → **Whose** book is this?
              Who owns this book?

---

why   → **Why** are you crying? What made you cry?

---

wide   → **Wide** means having a big distance from one side
              to the other side.
              The ocean is **wide.** It is a big distance from
              one side of the ocean to the other.

              The green line is **wide.** It is not thin or
              narrow. The orange line is **wider.** The blue
              line is **widest.** It is **wider** than the green or
              orange line.

---

will   → "**Will** you come to my party?" asked Claire.
              I answered, "Yes, I **will** come to your party.
              What time **will** the party begin?"

              → Red and white mixed together **will** make pink.
              When you mix together red and white, you **will**
              always get pink. Pink is the color they make.

              → How many marshmallows **will** you eat?
              How many marshmallows are you going to eat?

---

win   → To **win** means to **be the best in a contest.**
              Who **won** the pie-eating contest?
              Who **was** the **best?** Who ate the most pies?

              → To **win** also means to **get a prize.**
              What did you **win?** What **prize** did you **get?**

wind

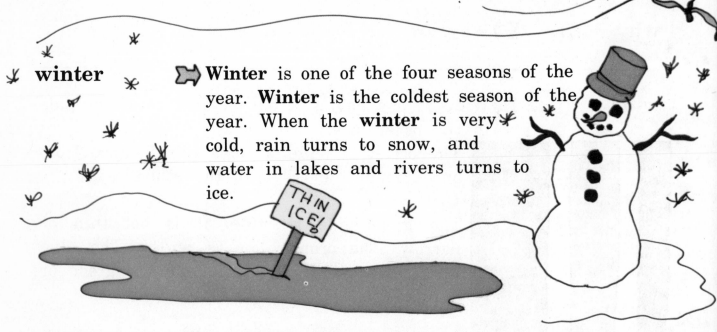

→ **Wind** is air that moves. To fly a kite, you need **wind.** When the **wind** is strong, we say that it is windy outside.

winter

→ **Winter** is one of the four seasons of the year. **Winter** is the coldest season of the year. When the **winter** is very cold, rain turns to snow, and water in lakes and rivers turns to ice.

THIN ICE!

wipe

→ To **wipe** means to **use a piece of cloth** or other soft thing **to clean.**

    After lunch, I **wiped** the table.

    After lunch, I **used a sponge to clean** the table. I rubbed the table until it was clean.

wire

→ A **wire** is a long, thin piece of metal. Some fences are made of **wire.** Some **wires** are used to carry electricity.

wish

→ To **wish** means to want to have something or to want something to happen.

    I am **wishing** for a set of trains.

    I would like a set of trains.

    Roger said, "I **wish** it would snow."

    Roger said, "I **hope** it will snow."

with

→ Ginny is speaking **with** her friend.
Ginny and her friend are speaking to one another.

→ Ken played **with** Sally. Ken and Sally played together.

→ Mix blue **with** yellow to make green.
Mix blue and yellow to make green.

→ I hit the ball **with** a bat.
I hit the ball using a bat.

→ Gary is the boy **with** curly black hair.
Gary is the boy who has curly black hair.

→ Do you have your gloves **with** you? Are you carrying your gloves?

---

woman

→ Carol's mother is a **woman.** Carol's aunt and grandmother are **women.** Carol is a girl. When she grows up, she will be a **woman.**

---

wood

→ **Wood** comes from trees. **Wood** is used to build houses, tables, chairs, and many other things. Sometimes **wood** is burned to make heat and light.

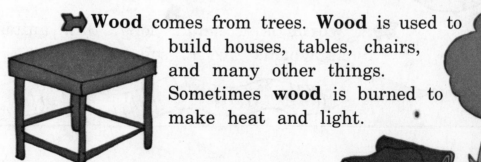

wool

→ **Wool** is the soft, thick hair of sheep and some other animals. **Wool** is used to make clothes, blankets, and other things.

word

➤ **Words** are the sounds we make when we talk. The sounds we call **words** can also be written. **Words** have meanings. By using **words,** you can tell people about yourself and other things. This book is written in **words.**

---

work

➤ I am **working** on a puzzle. I am trying to put all the pieces of the puzzle together.

➤ A fire fighter's **work** is to put out fires.
A fire fighter's **job** is to put out fires.

➤ Kevin **worked** the clay into a ball.
Kevin made the clay into a ball.

➤ My wristwatch **works.**
My wristwatch runs. It can tell me the time.

---

world

➤ The **world** is our earth. The **world** is made of land and water. All people, animals, and plants are a part of our **world.**

---

worm

➤ A **worm** is a small, long, thin animal.
Some **worms** live in soil.

---

worse

➤ **Worse** means **not as good** as another thing.
Diana's cold is **worse** today.
Diana's cold is **not as good** today as it was yesterday. She is not as well.

worst　　➤Worst means **not as good** as any other thing.
That cake is the **worst** I have eaten.
That cake is **not as good** as any other cake I have eaten.

---

would　　➤I **would** rather have chocolate than vanilla ice cream. I like chocolate ice cream.

➤On Saturday, we **would** go to the park.
On Saturday, we **used to** go to the park.

---

wrist　　➤Your **wrist** is a part of your body.
Your **wrist** is between your arm and your hand.

---

wristwatch　　➤A **wristwatch** is a small clock.
You wear a **wristwatch** on your wrist.

---

write　　➤To **write** means to **use a pen, pencil, or other writing tool** to put words or numbers on paper.
Toni can **write** her name.
Toni can **use a pencil** to make her name.
Toni can write "*Toni*."

---

wrong　　➤Wrong means **not right**.
1 + 3 = ?　　**4 5 6**

Two answers are **wrong**.
Two answers are **not right**.

X is the written sign that marks a spot on a pirate map. The X tells you where the treasure chest is buried.

X is a written sign that means **kisses**. **X's** on a letter mean you are sending **kisses** to someone. Doris wrote to her grandmother,

"Love and **kisses**. Love and **xxxxxx**."

xylophone

A **xylophone** is a musical instrument. **Xylophones** are made of bars of metal or wood. Each bar is a different size. To make music with a **xylophone**, you hit the bars.

218

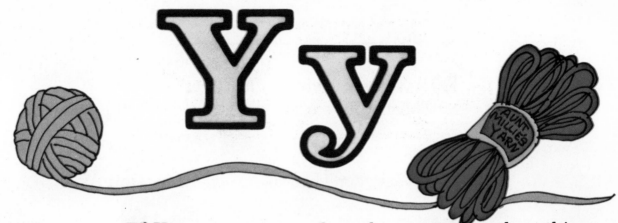

Yy

yarn

Yarn is strings of wool, cotton, or other things. **Yarn** is used to make clothes. **Yarn** comes in many colors.

year

A **year** is an amount of time. A **year** is 365 days long. A **year** is also twelve months long. The four seasons of the **year** are summer, fall, winter, and spring. Everyone has a birthday once each **year.**

How old are you? What is your age? Are you six **years** old?

yell

To **yell** means to **speak in a loud voice.**
Who is **yelling?** Who is **shouting?**
Who is **speaking in a loud voice?**

yellow

Yellow is a color. This is yellow. Daffodils are **yellow** flowers.

yes

The man asked Lewis, "Is your name Lewis?" Lewis said, "**Yes,** my name is Lewis."

219

yesterday

yesterday	➡ Hattie went swimming **yesterday**. Hattie went swimming the **day before today**.

---

yet	➡ Have you eaten lunch **yet**? Have you eaten lunch **before this time**?
	➡ Please don't go home **yet**. Please don't go home **at this time**.
	➡ It rained all day. It is raining **yet**. It is raining **still**.

---

you	➡ **You** is the word people use when **talking or writing to another** person. Ollie said to Felice, "How are **you** today?" Felice said, "I feel fine, thank **you**, Ollie." "I'm glad that **you are** feeling fine and that **you're** not sick," said Ollie. "**You will** be able to come to my party. **You'll** come to my party, won't **you?**" he asked.

---

young	➡ Children are **young** people. They are **not old**.

---

your	➡ **Your** means **belonging to you**. Are these **your** toys? Do they **belong to you**? Are these toys **yours**?

---

yourself	➡ Do you know how to tie your shoelaces by **yourself**? Can you tie your shoelaces with no one helping you?

Zz

zebra

> A **zebra** is an animal that looks like a small horse with black and white stripes.

zero

> **Zero** is a number. It is also written as **O. Zero** written alone means **none** or **nothing.**
>
> How many cookies do I have?
> I have **zero.** I have **none.**

> Sometimes, **zero** is written just after another number to make a new number that tells how many groups of ten there are.
>
> 10   means one group of ten.
> 40   means four groups of ten.
> 150   means fifteen groups of ten.

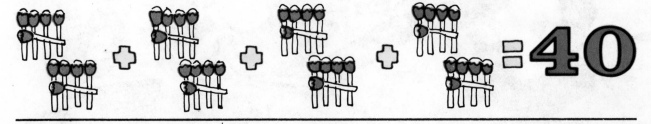

zipper

> A **zipper** keeps clothes and other things closed. **Zippers** are made of small pieces of metal or plastic held together by a piece of cloth.

A **zoo** is a place where animals from all over the world are kept. You can visit **zoos** to see and learn about these animals.

My Storybook

List of Stories and Poems

LITTLE RED RIDING HOOD

A little girl lived in a small house near a forest. Her mother had made her a pretty red cloak. It had a red hood. And the little girl liked it so much she wore it almost every day. So people called her Little Red Riding Hood.

On the other side of the forest was another small house. Little Red Riding Hood's grandmother lived there.

One fine day, Little Red Riding Hood's mother said: "Your grandmother is not very well. Here are some eggs and some butter. Take the basket to her, with my love. But be sure not to talk to anyone on the way. It will soon be dark. Then the wolves come out in the forest."

So Little Red Riding Hood put on her red cloak. She tied the red hood under her chin. And away she went.

Now the wild flowers in the woods

were very beautiful. Little Red Riding Hood stopped to look at them. "I know!" she said. "I will take some to grandmother." So she put her basket down and began to pick the flowers.

Soon it began to grow dark. Little Red Riding Hood remembered what her mother had said. So she started along the path again. She had just gone a few steps, when out jumped a big, gray wolf.

"Where are you going, little girl?" asked the wolf. He spoke very kindly.

Little Red Riding Hood thought he would not hurt her. So she told him she was taking some eggs and some butter to her grandmother. "She lives on the other side of the forest," she said.

"Aha!" thought the wolf. "I know where that is. I shall get there before you!" Then he said to Little Red Riding Hood: "Well, I had better let you go on."

So Little Red Riding Hood went on her way. At the same time the wolf ran as fast as he could. He took a shortcut

through the trees. Soon he was at the grandmother's house. He went up to the door and knocked.

"Who is it?" called the grandmother.

"It is Little Red Riding Hood," the wolf said in a voice that sounded a lot like Little Red Riding Hood's.

"Pull the handle and the latch will go up," the grandmother said.

The wolf pulled and the latch went up. Then he pushed open the door. He went up to the bed. The old lady lay in a white nightdress and with a cap on her head.

The grandmother saw that it was not Little Red Riding Hood, but a big, gray wolf. She let out a loud scream. The wolf opened his great mouth to eat her up. But the grandmother jumped out of bed, as fast as an old lady could. She ran outside. She ran and ran through the woods in her nightdress and cap.

The wolf was very angry that the grandmother had got away. But he didn't have time to think about it. He had to get ready for Little Red Riding Hood. He found one of the grandmother's nightdresses. When he had it on, he looked for a nightcap. He pulled this down over his head.

Then he jumped into bed and pulled the covers up to his chin.

It was not long before there was a knock at the door.

"Who is it?" called the wolf. Now he sounded like the grandmother.

"It is Little Red Riding Hood," said a voice on the other side of the door.

"Pull the handle and the latch will go up," the wolf said.

"Oh, grandmother," said Little Red Riding Hood as she came in, "how are you feeling today?"

"Ahem," the wolf said. "A little better, my dear. A little better. But shut the door well, my little lamb. Then come and sit close beside me."

Little Red Riding Hood sat down by the side of the bed.

"I have brought you some eggs and some butter and flowers," she said. She bent over the bed. "But grandmother, what big ears you have!"

"All the better to hear you with, my child," said the wolf.

"And what big eyes you have, grandmother!" Little Red Riding Hood said.

"All the better to see you with."

"And, oh, grandmother, what big teeth you have!" cried Little Red Riding Hood.

"All the better to eat you with!" cried the wolf. He jumped out of bed toward Little Red Riding Hood. His great mouth was wide open.

Little Red Riding Hood ran screaming toward the door. The wolf was right behind her. Just as he was about to get her, the door flew open. There was the grandmother and a woodcutter.

The woodcutter ran across the room toward the wicked wolf. With one stroke of his ax he killed him.

Then the grandmother held Red Riding Hood in her arms. She fed her cake and honey. After that the woodcutter took her home. And safe inside her house, Little Red Riding Hood told her mother everything that had happened.

SNOW WHITE AND THE SEVEN DWARFS

One winter's day, a gentle Queen sat by her window sewing. As she sewed she cut her finger. Two little drops of blood fell from it.

The Queen made a wish. "How I wish for a little daughter with cheeks as rosy as those drops of blood. May her skin be white as snow. May her hair be black as night."

To the Queen's great joy, her wish came true. She had a little daughter and named her Snow White.

Soon after this the Queen died. The King married another lady. She was very beautiful but very unkind. And every day she looked into her magic mirror and asked:

"Mirror, mirror, on the wall,
Who is the fairest of them all?"

The mirror would say:

"You, Queen, are fairest of them all."

The years passed. Snow White grew into a very lovely girl. One day the Queen looked into the mirror. To her great surprise it said:

"Fair and lovely though you are,
Snow White fairer is by far."

This made the Queen very angry. She called her servants. "Kill Snow White,"

she said. But the servants loved Snow White. They did not want to kill her. So one took her into the forest. He left her there and hoped that somebody would find her and take care of her.

Snow White walked alone in the forest. Then she came to a little cottage. She opened the door and went in. She found seven little beds, seven little glasses of wine, and seven loaves of bread. She ate a good dinner. Then she lay down and fell fast asleep.

This cottage belonged to seven dwarfs. When it was dark they came home and lit their seven lamps. Then they found Snow White.

"How beautiful she is!" they all said.

At this Snow White sat up in bed.

"Do not be afraid," said the dwarfs. "We are your friends. But, tell us, how did you come here?"

So Snow White told them her story

and the dwarfs said she could live with them.

"But," they said, "be careful. Keep the door locked while we are away. The Queen may find you and try to hurt you."

And the Queen did find out where Snow White was. She dressed herself up as an old woman. She went to the cottage. Soon Snow White heard somebody calling: "Fine things to sell! Fine things to sell!"

Snow White opened the window and looked out. She saw the old woman selling very pretty ribbons and laces. So she forgot what the dwarfs had said. She unlocked the door and ran out.

"I think I will buy some ribbons!" she said.

"Let me put them on your dress for you," said the old woman. Then she tied them very tight. Snow White fell down as if she were dead.

"That is the end of your beauty," said the Queen.

Soon the dwarfs came home. They saw Snow White and guessed what had happened. Quick as can be, one of them took out a knife. He cut the ribbons. In a few minutes Snow White was better.

When the Queen got back to the palace she went to her room. She took off the old woman's clothes. She put on a fine gown and a beautiful necklace. Then she looked into her magic mirror and asked:

"Mirror, mirror, on the wall,
Who is the fairest of them all?"

Much to her surprise the mirror said:

"Fair and lovely though you are,
Snow White fairest is by far."

So the Queen knew that Snow White was still alive. And she began to make another plan to kill her.

The seven dwarfs went away the next morning. They told Snow White again not to open the door to anyone.

The same morning the Queen painted her face. She dressed as a poor woman and went to the cottage. This time she took a beautiful apple. One side of it was filled with poison.

"Would you like this pretty apple?" she said. She held it up so Snow White could see it.

But Snow White was wiser now. She would not take it.

"Do you think it is poisoned?" said the old woman. "See, I shall eat part of it. That will show you it is good." And she took a bite from the side that was all right.

The apple looked beautiful. The old woman had eaten some of it. So Snow White held out her hand. She put the apple to her lips. But as soon as she took a bite she fell down on the floor.

Then the Queen went back to the palace. She asked her magic mirror:

"Mirror, mirror, on the wall,
Who is the fairest of them all?"

This time the mirror said:

"Thou, Queen, art fairest of
them all."

Then the Queen knew that Snow White
was dead at last.

At dusk the dwarfs went back to the
cottage. But they could not help Snow
White. She was dead. Sadly they put her
in a glass box. They set it on a hill for
everyone to see.

One day a Prince was passing by.
When he saw Snow White, he loved her
at once. So he gave the dwarfs a lot of
money to let him carry her box away.
But as it was being lifted, one of the men
carrying the box fell. The door of the box
flew open. The piece of apple fell out of
Snow White's mouth. She sat up at once.

The Prince was full of joy to find that
she was still alive. He had heard the
story of the Queen from the dwarfs.

Snow White gave the Prince her hand.
She went away with him to his father's
palace. They were married and lived
happily ever after.

The Queen was invited to the wedding. But she was so angry that Snow
White was alive that she fell down in a fit
and died.

THE ELEPHANT'S CHILD

In the High and Far-Off times the Elephant, O Best Beloved, had no trunk. He had only a nose, as big as a boot. He could wriggle it from side to side. But he couldn't pick up things with it. But there was one Elephant—a new Elephant—an Elephant's Child. He was full of curiosity. That meant he asked ever so many questions.

And he lived in Africa. He filled all Africa with his questions. He asked his tall aunt, the Ostrich, "Why do your tail feathers grow just so?" And his tall aunt spanked him with her hard, hard claw.

He asked his tall uncle, the Giraffe, "What makes your skin so spotty?" And his tall uncle spanked him with his hard, hard hoof. And still he was full of questions.

He asked his broad aunt, the Hippopotamus, "Why are your eyes so red?" And his broad aunt spanked him with her broad, broad hoof.

And he asked his hairy uncle, the Baboon, "Why do melons taste just so?" And his hairy uncle spanked him with his hairy, hairy paw. And still he was full of questions! He asked about everything that he saw, or heard, or felt, or touched. And all his uncles and his aunts spanked him.

One fine morning, in the middle of the morning, the Elephant's Child asked a fine new question. He had never asked it before. He asked, "What does the Crocodile have for dinner?" Then everybody said "Hush!" in a loud voice. And they spanked him at once without stopping, for a long time.

By and by, when that was done, he came upon Kolokolo Bird. He said, "My father has spanked me. My mother has spanked me. All my aunts and uncles have spanked me for all my questions. And still I want to know what the Crocodile has for dinner!"

The Kolokolo Bird said, "Go to the banks of the great Limpopo River and find out."

That very next morning, in the middle of the morning, the Elephant's Child took a hundred pounds of bananas (the little short red kind). He took a hundred pounds of sugarcane (the long purple kind). He took seventeen melons (the green crackly kind), and said to all his dear families, "Good-bye, I am going to the great Limpopo River to find out what the Crocodile has for dinner." And they all spanked him once more for luck—though he asked them very nicely to stop.

Then he went away—a little warm, but not at all unhappy, eating melons, and throwing the skins about, because he could not pick them up.

He went on and on, eating melons all the time. At last he came to the banks of the great Limpopo River.

Now you must know and understand, O Best Beloved, that until that very week, and day, and hour, and minute, this Elephant's Child had never *seen* a Crocodile. He did not know what one was like!

The first thing he found was a Rock-Snake curled round a rock.

"Excuse me," said the Elephant's Child very nicely. "Have you seen a Crocodile?"

"*Have* I seen a Crocodile?" said the Rock-Snake. "What will you ask me next?"

"Excuse me," said the Elephant's Child, "but could you tell me what he has for dinner?"

Then the Rock-Snake very quickly spanked the Elephant's Child.

"That is odd," said the Elephant's Child. "My father and my mother, and my uncle and my aunt, and my other aunt, the Hippopotamus, and my other uncle, the Baboon, have all spanked me for my questions. I guess this is the same thing."

So he said good-bye very nicely to the Rock-Snake and went on. He was a little warm, but not at all unhappy, eating melons, and throwing the skin about because he could not pick it up. Just then he stepped on what he thought was a log of wood. It was at the very edge of the great Limpopo River.

But it was really the Crocodile, O Best Beloved. And the Crocodile winked one eye!

"Excuse me," said the Elephant's Child very nicely, "but have you seen a Crocodile?"

Then the Crocodile winked the other eye. He lifted half his tail out of the mud. The Elephant's Child stepped back very nicely, because he did not want to be spanked again.

"Come here, Little One," said the Crocodile. "Why do you ask such things?"

"Excuse me," said the Elephant's Child. "But my father has spanked me. My mother has spanked me, and my tall aunt, the Ostrich, and my tall uncle, the Giraffe, who can kick ever so hard, as well as my broad aunt, the Hippopotamus, and my hairy uncle, the Ba-boon, *and* the Rock-Snake, just up the bank, who spanks harder than any of them. And so, if it's all the same to you, I don't want to be spanked any more."

"Come here, Little One," said the Crocodile, "for I am the Crocodile."

Then the Elephant's Child was very surprised. He knelt down on the bank and said, "You are the very one I have been looking for all these long days. Will you please tell me what you have for dinner?"

"Come here, Little One," said the Crocodile, "and I'll whisper."

Then the Elephant's Child put his head down close to the Crocodile's mouth. And the Crocodile caught him by his little nose, which up to that week, day, hour, and minute, had been no bigger than a boot.

"I think," said the Crocodile—and he said it between his teeth—"I think today I will begin with an Elephant's Child!"

At this, O Best Beloved, the Elephant's Child was very angry. And he said, talking through his nose, like this, "Led go! You are hurting be!"

Then the Rock-Snake came down from the bank and said, "My young friend, if you do not now, this very minute, pull as hard as ever you can, I think that your friend here (and by this he meant the Crocodile) will jerk you into the stream before you can say Jack Robinson."

This is the way Rock-Snakes always talk.

Then the Elephant's Child sat back. He pulled, and pulled, and pulled. His nose began to stretch. And the Crocodile went into the water. He made it all white with great sweeps of his tail. And *he* pulled, and pulled, and pulled.

And the Elephant's Child's nose kept on stretching. The Crocodile slapped his

tail like an oar. *He* pulled, and pulled, and pulled. At each pull the Elephant's Child's nose grew longer and longer— and it hurt him!

Then the Elephant's Child felt his legs slipping. He said through his nose, "This is too butch for be!"

Then the Rock-Snake came down the bank. He wrapped himself around the Elephant's Child's legs, and said, "Young friend, who asks so many questions, we must now pull very hard. Because if we do not, I feel you are headed for a ride down the river between a set of

teeth! This will make the rest of your life very difficult!"

That is the way all Rock-Snakes always talk.

So he pulled. The Elephant's Child pulled. The Crocodile pulled. But the Elephant's Child and the Rock-Snake pulled hardest. And at last the Crocodile let go of the Elephant's Child's nose with a plop. You could hear it all up and down the Limpopo.

The Elephant's Child sat down hard. But first he was careful to say "Thank you" to the Rock-Snake. Next he was kind to his poor pulled nose. He wrapped it all up in cool banana leaves, and hung it in the great Limpopo to cool.

"What are you doing that for?" said the Rock-Snake.

"Excuse me," said the Elephant's Child, "but my nose is badly out of shape. I am waiting for it to shrink."

"Then you will have to wait a long time," said the Rock-Snake. "Some people do not know what is good for them."

The Elephant's Child sat there for three days waiting for his nose to shrink. But it never got any shorter. For, O Best Beloved, you will see and understand that the Crocodile had pulled it out into a trunk—the same as all Elephants have today.

At the end of the third day a fly came and stung him on the shoulder. Before he knew what he was doing, the Elephant's Child picked up his trunk and hit that fly dead.

"Ah-ha!" said the Rock-Snake. "You couldn't have done that with your other nose. Try and eat a little now."

Before he thought what he was doing the Elephant's Child put out his trunk and picked up some grass. Then he put it into his own mouth.

"Ah-ha!" said the Rock-Snake. "You couldn't have done *that* with your other nose. Don't you think the sun is very hot here?"

"It is," said the Elephant's Child. And before he thought what he was doing he schlooped up a schloop of mud from the banks of the Limpopo. He slapped it on his head—it felt good behind his ears.

"See now?" said the Rock-Snake. "You couldn't have done that with your other nose. Now how do you feel about being spanked again?"

"Excuse me," said the Elephant's Child, "but I should not like it at all."

"How would you like to spank somebody?" said the Rock-Snake.

"I should like it very much!" said the Elephant's Child.

"Well," said the Rock-Snake, "you will find that new nose is very good for spanking."

"Thank you," said the Elephant's Child, "I'll remember that. And now I think I'll go home to all my dear families."

So the Elephant's Child went home across Africa. When he wanted to eat he pulled fruit down from a tree. He did not wait for it to fall as he used to do. When he wanted grass he picked grass up from the ground. He did not go on his knees as he used to do. When the flies bit him he slapped them dead. And he made himself a new, cool, mud-cap whenever the sun was hot. When he felt lonely he sang to himself down his trunk. The noise was louder than many brass bands.

He went out of his way to find a broad Hippopotamus (who was not part of his family), and he spanked her very hard—just to make sure the Rock-Snake was right about his new trunk. The rest of the time he picked up the melon skins he had dropped on his way—for he was very neat and tidy.

One dark evening he came back to all his dear families. He rolled up his trunk and said, "How do you do?" They were very glad to see him, and said, "Come here and be spanked for all your questions."

"Pooh," said the Elephant's Child, "I don't think you people know anything about spanking. But *I* do, and I'll show you."

Then he let down his trunk and

knocked two of his dear brothers head over heels.

"O Bananas!" said they. "Where did you learn that trick? And what have you done to your nose?"

"I got a new one from the Crocodile on the banks of the great Limpopo River," said the Elephant's Child. "I asked him what he had for dinner, and he gave me this to keep."

"It looks very ugly," said his hairy uncle, the Baboon.

"It does," said the Elephant's Child. "But it's very useful." He picked up his hairy uncle, the Baboon, by one of his hairy legs, and tossed him into a hornets' nest.

Then that bad Elephant's Child spanked all his dear families for a long time, until they were very warm and very unhappy. He pulled out his tall Ostrich aunt's tail feathers. He pulled his tall uncle, the Giraffe, through a thornbush. He shouted at his broad aunt, the Hippopotamus. He blew bubbles into her ear when she was sleeping in the water after meals. But he never let any one touch Kolokolo Bird.

At last his family couldn't take any more. So they went off one by one to the banks of the great Limpopo River to get new noses from the Crocodile. When they came back nobody spanked anybody any more. And ever since that day, O Best Beloved, all the Elephants you will ever see—and all those that you won't—have trunks just like the trunk of the Elephant's Child.

JACK AND THE BEANSTALK

Once there was a poor woman. She lived with her son Jack near a great wood. They were so poor that often Jack went to bed without any dinner. At last things got so bad that Jack's mother made up her mind to sell the cow. It was the one thing they had left. So, when market-day came, Jack set out. He took the cow with him.

On the way he met a man with a bag of beans. Jack liked the beans. He asked the man to give them to him.

"I cannot give them to you. But I might sell them," said the man.

"I do not have any money," said Jack. "But my mother has sent me to market to sell the cow. Come with me. When I have sold the cow I will give you half."

"No," said the man. "These are magic beans. You can have them if you give me the cow."

Jack said yes. So the man took the cow. And Jack ran home to show the beans to his mother. The poor woman cried when she heard the story. She was so angry at Jack that she threw the beans out of the window.

Jack went to bed very upset that night. But the next morning, he was surprised to find something in front of his window. It looked like a huge tree. He went near and found that the wonderful beans had grown up. They were now a very tall beanstalk. Indeed, the top of the stalk was almost out of sight.

Jack jumped on to the beanstalk. Higher and higher. Still higher he climbed. At last he reached the top. He found himself in a strange country. He walked along a little way. Then he met an old woman. Jack had never seen her before, but to his surprise she said:

"I know you quite well, Jack. Years ago, a wicked ogre killed your father. He took all the money which should be yours. This ogre lives close by. If you want to punish him I can help you."

Jack said that he did want to punish the ogre! "Where does he live?" he asked.

"In that castle over there," said the old woman. And with that she disappeared.

So Jack made his way to the castle. He climbed the steps and rang the bell. A woman opened the door. Jack asked for a room for the night.

"Oh, no!" said the woman, "I cannot take you in. My husband is an ogre. If he finds you here he will kill you and eat you."

"But can't you hide me?" asked Jack.

"I will do my best," said the woman. "But you must go away first thing in the morning."

Jack promised. So she took him into the kitchen and gave him a good meal. Then there came a great knock at the door.

"Quick!" cried the woman. "Jump into the oven. Don't make a sound until my husband has gone to bed."

In went Jack and a minute later the ogre came into the room. In a terribly loud voice he said:

"Fee, fi, fo, fum!
I smell the blood of an
    Englishman;
Be he alive, or be he dead,

I'll grind his bones to make
my bread!"

Jack was very afraid. But the wife said, "Don't be silly, my dear. See what a nice dinner I made."

The dinner was so good that the ogre sat down and ate it all up. Then he told his wife to bring in his favorite hen. She went outside and came back with a beautiful hen. She put it on the table.

"Lay an egg!" said the ogre. The hen laid a golden egg.

"What a useful bird!" thought Jack.

He looked through a crack in the oven door.

Soon after this the ogre fell asleep. He snored so loudly that he shook the halls. As soon as Jack heard the snores, he came out of his hiding place. He picked up the hen and ran away. He ran and ran until he reached the beanstalk. Then he climbed down as fast as he could go. When he reached the ground he told his mother what had happened. She was very happy, and called Jack her "brave boy." They sold the golden eggs which the hen laid. And they lived well for

some time on the money they were able to get for them.

But after a while Jack wanted to go up the beanstalk again. So one day he disguised himself as well as he could, and climbed up. He found his way to the castle. Again, he asked the ogre's wife to give him a room for the night. But the woman said, "No. The last time I helped a poor boy, he stole the ogre's favorite hen!" But Jack begged so hard that she gave in. This time she hid him in a cupboard.

Soon the ogre returned to the castle.

As he came into the kitchen, he cried out in his terribly loud voice:

"Fee, fi, fo, fum!
I smell the blood of an
Englishman;
Be he alive, or be he dead,
I'll grind his bones to make
my bread!"

"Don't be silly, my dear!" said the wife. "See what a fine dinner I made for you."

The ogre sat down and ate his supper. When he was done, he roared: "Bring me my money-bags!"

His wife put the bags on the table. The ogre counted his money. Then he put the coins back into the bags and fell asleep. Out jumped Jack. He took the money-bags and ran out of the castle. Soon he was back again at home.

"Have fun spending all this money, mother," he said. He pulled the bags out of his pockets one by one. "An ogre killed father and took it from him. The money is really ours."

Some time after this, Jack climbed the beanstalk again. He walked to the castle. This time he dared not let the ogre's wife see him. So he waited for some hours. Then he got in and hid himself in the broom closet. When the ogre came home he said:

"Fee, fi, fo, fum,
    I smell the blood of an
        Englishman!
Be he alive, or be he dead,
    I'll grind his bones to make
        my bread!"

"Oh, no!" said his wife. "You always think there is someone in the house. This time I know you are wrong."

When the ogre had eaten his dinner, he called for his harp. His wife set it on the table. At a word from the ogre, it began to play by itself. This so pleased Jack that he wanted the harp very much.

As soon as the ogre was asleep, Jack jumped up. He took the harp and ran out of the room. But the harp called out: "Master! Master!"

The ogre woke up. He ran after Jack! Looking over his shoulder, Jack could see the giant. The ground shook with every step the giant took. The beanstalk seemed a long way off. But Jack would not give up. Closer and closer came the giant. Faster and faster ran Jack. And then, Jack reached the beanstalk. He began to climb down very quickly. By the time he had reached the ground, the ogre was halfway down.

Jack said: "Mother, bring the ax! The ogre's coming!"

Jack watched in horror as the beanstalk swayed from side to side. The giant's roars filled the air.

"Hurry, mother, hurry!" said Jack. "The giant is almost upon us!"

Out ran Jack's mother with the ax. Jack took it and cut the beanstalk right through with a single blow. The ogre fell down with a crash. And that was the end of his life.

Jack and his mother lived many happy years after that. When Jack grew up he fell in love with a beautiful princess and married her. By that time he was a rich man. His deeds had made him famous.

DICK WHITTINGTON AND HIS CAT

Dick Whittington was a poor country boy. He had lost his father and mother. So he was alone in the world. He had to make a living as best he could. His only friend was a cat. He had fed it when it was hungry. And it was a very good friend to him.

Dick had once met a man. The man said the streets of London were made of gold. So Dick went to London. But when he got there, he saw that the streets were made of hard stones. And there were poor people in rags. Now Dick had nowhere to go. So he had to sleep with his cat on the hard stones for many nights.

At last Dick got a job. He helped clean the house of a rich man. But he was not very happy there. The cook was a wicked woman. She beat him every day. She also made him sleep in a room which was overrun with rats and mice. But Dick's cat soon killed them.

Now, the rich man was a trader. He used to fill his ships with all kinds of goods. Then he sent them to countries far away. The goods were sold for a lot of money. And, being a kind man, he let his servants put things to sell on his ships.

One day, the man was about to send a ship to the Indies. His daughter, Alice, said to Dick: "What are you going to sell?"

"I've only my cat," said Dick.

"Well, sell your cat," said Alice.

And to please Alice, Dick parted with the only friend he had in the world.

But Dick soon began to miss his cat.

The rats and mice came back to his room. They kept him awake at night. The cook beat him more than ever. Dick's life was very hard. So one morning he left to walk back to the country.

Dick got as far as the village of Highgate. But he was very tired. So he sat on a stone to rest. Far below he could see the rooftops of London. The bells began to ring. And the sound carried across the fields.

"Turn a-gain, Whitt-ing-ton,
    Thrice Mayor of London."

That was what the ding-ding-dong of the bells seemed to say to him. Poor Dick tried to laugh. Then he began to cry.

But soon he said to himself: "After all, it is only the cook who treats me badly. Alice speaks to me! She is nice. I will turn again, as the bells say, and see what happens."

So he went back to the rich man's house. And there he had good news. The ship was back. His cat had been sold at a very high price. Here is how it happened.

When the ship landed, the captain went to see the King of the country. He was asked to stay for dinner. There he saw surprising things. As soon as the dishes were put on the tables, rats and mice came and ate all the food.

"Oh, dear!" cried the King. "I shall not get anything to eat again today."

"Goodness," said the captain. "You ought to have a cat. It would kill all these rats and mice."

"A cat?" said the King. "What's that? Is it a new kind of lion? I have hundreds of lions and tigers. None of them would kill a mouse for me."

The captain sent a sailor to get Dick Whittington's cat. When the King saw it kill rat after rat and mouse after mouse, he clapped his hands. He shouted with joy. He said that he would buy it—even if the cat cost him half his kingdom!

"Will you take six sacks of gold for this wonderful little animal?" he asked the captain.

The captain said yes. And the ship came to London with the sacks of gold.

The wicked cook said that Dick was only a poor boy. He did not have a friend in the world. So there was no need to give him the gold. But the rich man was honest. He gave Dick all the money. He also took care of him as if he were his own son. Years later Dick married Alice. He actually became Mayor of London four times (once more than the bells had said). So goes the story of Dick Whittington, who really *was* a Mayor of London.

THESEUS AND THE MINOTAUR

Theseus was the son of Aegeus—a King who lived in the city of Athens. While he was a child, Theseus lived with his mother, Aethra.

One day, Theseus was grown into a strong young man. Aethra took him to a great mountain. There she pointed to a huge rock. She told Theseus to lift it. When he had done so, he found a pair of sandals and a sword. Aethra said the sword and sandals had been put there by his father, Aegeus. Now Theseus must put them on and go to find his father.

At that time, travelers on the road were often killed by robbers. So Theseus was told to go by sea. But Theseus felt very brave with his father's sword. So he did not listen.

On the road, Theseus killed four robbers who had hurt many people. When he finally got to Athens, he found that everyone was talking about him. He was the brave young man who had killed the robbers. Yet one person knew nothing of this. Theseus's father had not heard that his son was in the city. He also did not know his son had killed the robbers.

So when Theseus went to the palace, he was a stranger to Aegeus. But Medea, the beautiful sorceress, knew who he was. Medea was a wicked woman. She had a son she wished to make King. But she knew that Aegeus would make Theseus King. So she planned a way to kill him.

Medea went to Aegeus. She said a young man was waiting to see him. She also said that he had come to Athens to kill him. Then Medea said she would give this man a cup of poison. The King

agreed to Medea's plan. But when Aegeus saw the young man, he looked at the sword by his side. Just as Theseus put the cup to his lips, the King said, "Stop!" He knew that Theseus was his son. And he was very glad to see him. The sorceress Medea ran from the city, never to return.

Now Theseus was happy. But it did not last. This is why. Many years before, King Minos of Crete had a son. And the son was killed while he was in Athens. This made Minos very sad and angry. So every nine years he made the people of Athens give him fourteen young men and women. One day when Theseus was with his father the message came. It was time to send the young men and women to Crete.

All Athens was sad and silent. Theseus's father was troubled. Theseus asked what would happen to the young people. Aegeus told him that they would be fed to the Minotaur—a horrible monster with a man's body and the head of a bull.

When Theseus heard this, he told his father he would go. Aegeus said, "No, you cannot." But Theseus did not listen. He went with the young men and women to Crete.

The ship they took had black sails. King Aegeus—hoping that his son might come back—gave Theseus a white sail. He was to use it if he was on the ship when it returned to Athens. Then King Aegeus would know whether or not his son was alive.

Theseus was sure they would be all right. So he did his best to make the other young people less afraid. Soon they got to Crete. They were taken before King Minos. Theseus told King Minos that he had come to kill the Minotaur.

The King laughed. He told Theseus that the monster would eat him alive. But Theseus spoke again. He said, "I am not afraid. I will go to meet the Minotaur. If I kill him, set the young people free. Never again ask the people of Athens to send men and women to Crete."

The King laughed again. But he agreed to this plan. He was sure Theseus could never escape from the maze where the Minotaur lived. He also told Theseus that he must go without his sword.

Now the prisoners were thrown into the dungeon. They would wait until they were sent one by one to the Minotaur. As they were being led out, Minos's daughter, Ariadne, threw herself at her father's feet. She begged him to let the young people go. Their deaths would make so many people sad. They were too young to die. King Minos did not listen to his daughter.

Night in the dungeon was more awful than the day. It was cold and damp. They could hear the Minotaur roaring.

But during the night, Ariadne came to the dungeon. She called softly to Theseus. She said she would help him kill the monster and gave him a short sword. Then Ariadne told Theseus that

while he might kill the Minotaur, he could be lost in the maze forever. So she gave him a large ball of string. "When you go through the maze," she said, "unroll the string. Then you will be able to find your way out again."

Theseus took the sword and the string. In the morning the guards came to the dungeon. They led Theseus to the maze and put him inside.

On the outside, the maze looked like a great circle. It had marble walls. But when Theseus was inside, he found that there were many paths. Walking slowly, Theseus first went one way. Then another. He let out the ball of string. Many paths he took ended in a wall. There was nothing to be seen but walls on each side of him. Now and then he heard a great roar.

At last Theseus came to the middle of the maze. Here was the dreadful Minotaur. It stood before him—with its ugly face and big shaggy body. They stared at each other. Then Theseus ran at him with his sword drawn. Theseus put his sword into the monster's body. The Minotaur fell dead at his feet.

When King Minos heard that Theseus was alive, he was very surprised. But he was ready to keep his word. So Theseus set sail for Athens with the other young men and women. All went well on the trip. But Theseus forgot to put up the white sail.

King Aegeus had watched the sea for days. At last he saw the ship. It had black sails. Thinking that his dear son was dead, he threw himself into the sea to his death. When the young people landed, there was sadness instead of joy.

Theseus brought his mother, Aethra, to Athens, where he ruled his father's kingdom for many years.

THE ELVES AND THE SHOEMAKER

A shoemaker lived with his wife. They had one room above his shop. Times were hard. Only a few people had enough money to spend on new shoes. So the shoemaker and his wife grew poorer. One day the wife had only bread for supper. The shoemaker had only enough leather to make one pair of shoes.

That night the shoemaker cut out his last pair of shoes. Then he went upstairs. He and his wife ate some bread and drank some water. They went sadly to bed.

The next morning, the shoemaker went down to his shop. He was going to make up the shoes. But when he got there the shoes were already sewn! For some time he scratched his head. "How could that happen?" he said. Then he picked up each shoe and looked at it. The shoes were as neat and well made as could be.

In a little while a gentleman came into the shop. He asked to see a pair of shoes. The shoemaker showed him the ones that had been made during the night. The man was very pleased with them. So he gave the shoemaker a good price—

more than the shoemaker was going to ask.

As soon as the gentleman had gone, the shoemaker put on his coat. He went out to buy enough leather to make two pairs of shoes. He also got a piece of meat for himself and his wife. When he returned, he cut out two pairs of shoes.

The next morning the shoemaker got out of bed. He ran down to sew up the leather he had cut out the night before.

Once again, he had a surprise. There were *two* pairs of shoes. They were ready to put on! The shoemaker was very surprised. He rubbed his eyes. This must be a dream! But no. When he looked again, the shoes were still there. He shook his head. He looked at each pair. There was nothing wrong with them. And how fine they looked!

The shoemaker put the shoes back on

the table. And in walked two gentlemen! They asked the shoemaker if he had some shoes. When the gentlemen tried the shoes, they gave the shoemaker a lot of money for them. This time the shoemaker didn't wait to put on his coat. He ran out and bought enough leather to make four pairs of shoes! He got a fat chicken for supper. And when he went back to the shop he cut out the leather. He left it on the table as before. When he came down next morning the leather had again been made into shoes.

This went on for quite some time. The shoemaker would cut the leather and leave it. When he went down in the morning the shoes were made up.

One night, the shoemaker and his wife had had a good dinner. They were falling asleep by the fire. Then the shoemaker sat up.

"This is a wonderful thing that has happened to us," he said to his wife. "But I don't understand it. Who is helping us? I think we should sit up tonight and see what goes on."

So the shoemaker and his wife did not go to bed. They went down to the shop and hid. Just then the village clock struck twelve. They saw the door open and in came two little elves. They were no bigger than small children. They had on short pants, even though the night was cold.

As soon as they sat down they went to work. They sang to themselves and worked until the shoes were done. Then, before the shoemaker and his wife could blink, they were gone.

"My, my," said the shoemaker's wife. "The poor things don't have any warm clothes. I shall make them some."

Then the shoemaker and his wife went to bed. The next morning the wife started to sew. By evening she had made two shirts, two pairs of long pants, and two jackets. The shoemaker had also been busy. He had made two pairs of little shoes. After they had had their supper, they put the clothes and shoes on the work table. Then they hid.

Again, the village clock struck twelve. In came the two little elves. When they jumped up on the table, they saw the clothes. On went the shirts. On went the long pants. On went the jackets and the shoes. Looking at each other, the two elves danced happily. Then, just as quickly as they had come, they were gone.

The next morning, the shoemaker worked hard. He had to make up the leather he had left on the table the night before. And just before he went to supper, he cut out more leather. But when he went down to his shop the next morning the leather was still there—just as he had left it.

The elves never again came to visit the shoemaker's shop. But the shoemaker and his wife still did well. In fact, they both lived happily ever after.

BABA YAGA AND THE LITTLE GIRL WITH THE KIND HEART

Once upon a time there was an old man. His wife was dead so he lived alone with his little daughter. They were very happy together. They used to smile at each other over a table piled with bread and jam. Everything went well. But then the old man took it into his head to marry again.

Yes, the old man took a wife. And so the poor little girl had a stepmother. And after that everything changed. There was no more bread and jam on the table. There was no more playing bo-peep. And the stepmother was not very nice. She blamed the girl for everything that went wrong. And the old man believed his new wife. So there were no more kind words for his little daughter. Day after day the stepmother said the little girl was too naughty to sit at the table. She would throw her some bread. "Go eat it somewhere else," she would say.

And the poor little girl used to go away by herself. She wet the dry bread with her tears. How she cried. Ah me! She cried for the old days. She cried over the days that were to come.

Mostly she wept because she was all alone. But one day she found a little friend in the shed. She was sitting in the corner eating her bread. Then she heard a little noise. It was like this: "Scratch—scratch."

And out came a little mouse. He had a little pointed nose, long whiskers, little round ears and bright eyes—and a very long tail. Then he sat up on his back legs. He curled his tail twice around him and looked at the little girl.

The little girl forgot all her troubles. She threw a piece of her bread to the little mouse. The mouse ate and ate and then it was gone. He looked for another piece. So she gave him another. Soon that was gone. And another and another. Then there was no bread left for the little girl. Well, she didn't mind that. She was very happy seeing the little mouse eating.

The mouse looked up with his little bright eyes. "Thank you," he said, in a little voice. "Thank you," he said. "You are a kind little girl. I am only a mouse, and I've eaten all your bread. But there is one thing I can do for you. That is to tell you to take care! Your stepmother is sister to Baba Yaga, the witch. So if ever she sends you to see Baba Yaga, you tell me. She will eat you with her iron teeth if you do not know what to do."

"Oh, thank you," said the little girl. Just then she heard the stepmother calling. She said, "Come in here. Clean up the tea dishes. Tidy the house. Sweep the floor, and clean everybody's boots."

So off she had to go.

When she went in, she had a good look at her stepmother. Sure enough she had a long nose. She was as bony as a fish. And the little girl thought of Baba Yaga and felt afraid. But she did not feel so bad when she remembered the mouse in the shed.

The very next morning it happened. The old man went off to see a friend in the village. As soon as the old man had gone, the stepmother called the little girl.

"Today you are to go to your dear aunt in the forest," she said. "Ask her for a needle and thread."

"But here is a needle and thread," says the little girl.

"Keep quiet," said the stepmother. She clicked her teeth, and made an ugly face. "Keep quiet," she said. "Didn't I tell you? You are to go to your dear little aunt."

"How shall I find her?" said the little girl. She was ready to cry. She knew her aunt was Baba Yaga, the witch.

The stepmother took hold of the little girl's nose and pinched it.

"That is your nose," she said. "Can you feel it?"

"Yes," said the poor little girl.

"You must go along the road into the forest. You will come to a fallen tree. Turn left. Then follow your nose and you will find her," said the stepmother. "Now, be off with you, lazy one. Here is some food for you to eat by the way." She gave the little girl some food wrapped up in a towel.

The little girl wanted to go tell the mouse she was going to Baba Yaga. She wanted to ask what she should do! But she looked back. And there was the stepmother watching her. So she had to go on.

She walked along the road through the forest. She came to the fallen tree. Then she turned to the left. Her nose was still hurting where the stepmother had pinched it. So she knew she had to go straight ahead. Then she heard a little noise.

"Scratch—scratch."

And out jumped the little mouse. He sat up in the road in front of her.

"Oh mouse, mouse," said the little girl, "my stepmother has sent me to her sister. I do not know what to do."

"It will not be hard," said the little mouse, "because of your kind heart. Take all the things you find in the road. Do with them what you like. Then you

will get away from Baba Yaga. Everything will be well."

"Are you hungry, mouse?" said the little girl.

"A little, I think," said the mouse.

The little girl undid the towel. There
was nothing in it but stones. That was
what the stepmother had given her to
eat!

"Oh, I'm so sorry," said the little girl.
"There's nothing to eat."

"Isn't there?" said the mouse. And as
she looked at them the stones turned to
bread and jam. The little girl sat down
on the fallen tree. The little mouse sat
beside her. They ate bread and jam until
they were not hungry any more.

"Keep the towel," said the little
mouse. "I think you might need it. And
remember what I said about the things
you find on on the way. And now good-
bye."

"Good-bye," said the little girl.

The little girl ran along. She found a
nice new handkerchief lying in the road.
So she picked it up and took it with her.
Then she found a little bottle of oil. She
picked it up and took it with her. Then
she found some bits of meat.

"I'd better take them too," she said.

Then she found a gay blue ribbon. She
took that. Then she found a little loaf of
good bread, and she took that too.

"I guess somebody will like this," she
said.

And then she came to the hut of Baba
Yaga, the witch. There was a high fence
around it with big gates. When she
pushed them open they squeaked, as if it
hurt them to move. The little girl was
sorry for them.

"How lucky," she said, "that I picked
up the bottle of oil!" She put the oil into
the hinges of the gates.

Inside the fence was Baba Yaga's hut.
It stood on hen's legs and walked about
the yard. And in the yard there was
Baba Yaga's servant. She was crying because of the things Baba Yaga made her
do. She wiped her eyes on her skirt.

"How lucky," said the little girl. "I
have a handkerchief!" And she gave the
handkerchief away. The servant wiped
her eyes on it and smiled through her
tears.

Close by the hut was a very thin dog.
It was eating some dry bread.

"How lucky," said the little girl, "that
I picked up a loaf!" And she gave the
loaf to the dog. He licked his lips.

The little girl went up to the hut. She
knocked on the door.

"Come in," said Baba Yaga.

The little girl went in. There was Baba
Yaga, the witch, sitting at a loom! In a
corner was a thin black cat. He was
watching a mouse-hole.

"Good day to you, auntie," said the little girl. She tried not to shake.

"Good day to you," said Baba Yaga.

"My stepmother has sent me to you.
She would like a needle and thread."

"Very well," said Baba Yaga. She
smiled and showed her iron teeth. "You
sit down here at the loom. Go on with my
weaving. I will go and get the needle and
thread."

The little girl sat down at the loom and
began to weave.

Baba Yaga went out. She called to her
servant. "Go, make a hot bath and wash
my niece. Get her clean. I'll make a fine
meal of her."

The servant came in for the jug. The
little girl said, "Don't be too quick in
making the fire. Carry the water in a
sieve." The servant smiled, but said nothing. She was afraid of Baba Yaga. But

she took a very long time about getting the bath ready.

Baba Yaga came to the window and asked:

"Are you weaving, little niece? Are you, my pretty?"

"I am, auntie," said the little girl.

When Baba Yaga went away, the little girl spoke to the thin black cat.

"What are you doing, thin black cat?"

"Watching for a mouse," said the thin black cat. "I haven't had any food for three days."

"How lucky," said the little girl, "that I picked up the bits of meat!" And she gave them to the thin black cat. The thin black cat ate them up, and said to the little girl:

"Little girl, do you want to get out of here?"

"Cat, dear, I do! Baba Yaga is going to eat me with her iron teeth."

"Well," said the cat, "I will help you."

Just then Baba Yaga came to the window.

"Are you weaving, little niece?" she asked. "Are you, my pretty?"

"I am, auntie," said the little girl, working away. The loom went clickety clack, clickety clack.

Baba Yaga went away.

The thin black cat said, "You have a comb in your hair. You have a towel. Take them and run for it while Baba Yaga is in the bathhouse. When Baba Yaga chases after you, you must listen. When she is close to you, throw away the towel. It will turn into a big, wide river. That will slow her down. But you must listen again. As soon as she is close to you throw away the comb. It will become a forest that she will never get through."

"But she'll hear the loom stop," said the little girl.

"I'll see to that," said the thin black cat.

The cat took the little girl's place at the loom.

Clickety clack, clickety clack. The loom never stopped for a moment.

The little girl looked to see that Baba Yaga was in the bathhouse. Then she jumped down from the little hut. She ran to the gates as fast as she could.

The big dog jumped up to tear her to pieces. But then he saw who she was.

"Why, this is the little girl who gave me the loaf," he said. "Have a good trip, little girl!" And he lay down again with his head between his paws.

She came to the gates. They opened quietly, quietly—without making any noise at all—because of the oil she had put into their hinges.

Outside the gates there was a little birch tree. It hit her so in the eyes that she could not go by.

"How lucky," said the little girl, "that I picked up the ribbon!" And she tied up the birch tree with the pretty blue ribbon. The birch tree was so pleased it stood still, looking at the ribbon. The little girl ran by.

How she did run!

Meanwhile the thin black cat sat at the loom. Clickety clack, clickety clack, sang the loom. But you never saw such a mess as the mess made by the thin black cat.

And soon Baba Yaga came to the window.

"Are you weaving, little niece?" she asked. "Are you, my pretty?"

"I am, auntie," said the thin black cat, while the loom went clickety clack, clickety clack.

"That's not the voice of my little dinner!" said Baba Yaga. She jumped into the hut, her iron teeth clicking. There was no little girl. Only the thin black cat sat at the loom, making a big mess.

"Grr," said Baba Yaga. She jumped for the cat, and began to hit it. "Why didn't you tear the little girl's eyes out?"

"In all these years," said the cat, "you have given me only one little bone. The kind little girl gave me bits of meat."

Baba Yaga threw the cat into a corner. Then she went out into the yard.

"Why didn't you squeak when she opened you?" she asked the gates.

"Why didn't you tear her to pieces?" she asked the dog.

"Why did you let her go by?" she asked the birch tree.

"Why were you so long in getting the bath ready? If you had been quicker, she never would have got away," said Baba Yaga to the servant. And she ran about the yard, beating them all.

"Ah!" said the gates, "in all these

years you never helped us work. But the kind little girl put good oil into our hinges."

"Ah!" said the dog, "in all these years you never threw me anything but crusts of bread. The kind little girl gave me a good loaf!"

"Ah!" said the little birch tree, "in all these years, you never gave me anything. The kind little girl tied me up with a gay blue ribbon."

"Ah!" said the servant, "in all these years, you have never given me a rag. But the kind little girl gave me a pretty handkerchief."

Baba Yaga clicked her iron teeth at them. She jumped into her bucket-broom and sat down. Then she drove off, sweeping her tracks behind her.

The little girl ran and ran. She put her ear to the ground and listened. Bang, bang, bang! She could hear Baba Yaga beating the broom to make it go faster. Baba Yaga was quite close. There she was, beating and sweeping coming along the road.

As fast as she could, the little girl took out the towel. She threw it on the ground. And the towel grew bigger and bigger. It got wetter and wetter. Soon there was a deep river between Baba Yaga and the little girl.

The little girl turned and ran. How she ran!

Baba Yaga came driving up on her broom. But the broom could not hold her up in the river. Baba Yaga was too heavy. She tried to get across. But she only got wet for her trouble. She clicked her iron teeth. They sounded like bricks falling down a chimney. Then she went home. She got together all her cows and drove them to the river.

"Drink, drink!" She screamed at them. The cows drank up the river. And Baba Yaga jumped on her broom again. She drove across the dry bed of the river. "I'll get you now!" she yelled.

The little girl put her ear to the ground and listened. Bang, bang, bang! She could hear Baba Yaga beating the broom. Nearer and nearer came the noise. Baba Yaga was beating and sweeping and coming along the road close behind.

The little girl threw down the comb. It grew bigger and bigger. Its teeth grew into a thick forest—so thick that not even Baba Yaga could get through. And Baba Yaga clicked her teeth and screamed. She was so angry! But all she could do was turn around and go home.

The little girl ran on home. But she was afraid to see her stepmother. So she ran into the shed.

"Scratch—scratch!" Out came the little mouse.

"So you got away all right, my dear," said the little mouse. "Now run in. Don't be afraid. Your father is back. You must tell him all about it."

The little girl went into the house.

"Where have you been?" said her father. "Why are you so out of breath?"

The stepmother turned yellow when she saw her. Her eyes glowed. Her teeth clicked together until they broke.

But the little girl was not afraid. She went to her father and climbed on his knee. Then she told him everything just as it had happened. And when the old man heard what his wife had done, he was so angry he drove her out of the hut. And after that he lived alone with the little girl. It was much better for both of them.

TALES OF KING ARTHUR

The Coming of Arthur

In the days of King Uther Pendragon, there were many wars. They were between knights and their Kings. During one, a wizard named Merlin came to Uther's kingdom. He showed him his magical powers. And he was made the King's counselor. Then Merlin told the King how to bring peace to the land. But he knew that there would danger again.

When King Uther married, Merlin said, "Give your first son to me. I will keep him safe." So when the King's son was born he was named Arthur. And Merlin took the baby to a knight called Sir Ector. He told Sir Ector to raise Arthur as though he were his own son.

After some years had passed, King Uther died. There were many who wanted to be King. Then one day there was a large stone in a London churchyard. A sword was stuck in it. On it were these words, "Who so pulleth out this sword is rightful King of England."

All the lords of the land went to this place. They tried to pull out the sword. They camped nearby. They all watched each other try. To pass the time, they also had games called jousts.

One day Sir Ector came to London with his son Kay and fifteen-year-old Arthur. Kay forgot his sword, so he asked Arthur to get it for him from the inn. The inn was locked so Arthur went to the church. There he saw the sword stuck in the stone. He pulled it out with no trouble. Now Sir Ector knew it was time to tell Arthur that he was King Uther's son.

At first the lords didn't want Arthur as their King. The sword was put back in the stone. Once again no one could pull it out except Arthur. Finally he was made King. He promised to rule the land well for the rest of his days.

Excalibur

After being hurt in a battle, King Arthur found that he had no sword.

"No matter," said Merlin. "Nearby there is a sword that shall be yours."

They rode on until they came to a lake. There Arthur saw an arm in the middle of the water. It held a sword in its hand. Then he saw a maiden rowing over the water.

Arthur called out, "Lady of the Lake! If that sword is yours I pray that you give it to me. I will give you treasure in return."

"Take the sword, King," said the Lady. "I will ask my gift in my own time."

Arthur then took the Lady's boat. He rowed out to the middle of the lake. When he reached the arm, the hand gave him the sword. Then the hand went back into the water.

Merlin told Arthur that the sword was called Excalibur. In battle it would shine like fire. It would also keep him from losing blood.

With this sword Arthur conquered Scotland, Ireland, Gaul, and Norway. He ruled well. He helped the poor and brought peace to the land. The people loved him. But soon his enemies began to plot his ruin.

King Arthur's Knights of the Round Table

In the days of King Arthur, the most beautiful lady was said to be Guinevere. She was the daughter of another King. Arthur sent Sir Lancelot, his best knight, to ask her to be his Queen. Her father was happy that his daughter should be wed to Arthur. So he told her to go to Camelot, where Arthur had set up his court.

On the trip Lancelot was very kind. Guinevere grew to love him. Lancelot loved her, too. But he did not tell her. And so Guinevere was married to King Arthur. Lancelot had done his job well. So he was made the Queen's champion. This meant he had to guard her life.

Now Guinevere's father had sent King Arthur a great round table. There was room for 150 knights. And Arthur said only the best knights should have a seat at it. There was no higher honor in the land than to be one of the Knights of the Round Table. Money could not buy a place there. So the knights at King Arthur's court had to prove how good they were by overcoming the evils of the land. The most famous knights were Sir Tristram, Sir Gawain, and Arthur's foster-brother, Sir Kay. Sir Galahad was the best knight of them all.

The Passing of Arthur

Mordred, King Arthur's nephew, was an evil man. He said that Queen Guinevere was wicked. He lied about her so she would be put to death. The plan worked. King Arthur felt he had to punish her.

Lancelot was away. But soon he heard the news. As the Queen was being led to her death he rode up, struck down her guards and carried her off. He and Guinevere could never come back to the kingdom.

Then Mordred got his men together and fought against Arthur. Mordred lost twice. But he fought again. Gawain was killed in the first battle. But before he died he sent word to Lancelot. He asked him to come to the King's aid. Before Lancelot heard, a third battle took place.

This fight was very bad. Arthur and two brothers, Lucan and Bedivere, were the only ones left of the army. Arthur had killed Mordred. But Mordred had given Arthur a bad wound. The knights carried the King to a little chapel and there Lucan died.

Arthur was very sad. He said, "Were I to live after them my life would only be sorrow. Take Excalibur and throw it into the lake."

Bedivere took the sword. But he did not have the heart to throw it into the lake. He thought nobody would know. So he hid it and returned to the King. Arthur asked what he had seen. Bedivere said that he had seen nothing but the lake.

"You have not done it," said the King. "Go and do as I ask."

Bedivere went. But again he did not put the sword in the lake. Then Arthur became angry and said, "You care more for the sword than for your King."

At that Bedivere ran out. He took the sword and threw it into the lake. Before it fell an arm caught the sword.

Arthur heard what had happened. Then he knew that Bedivere had told the truth. He told Bedivere to help him to the lake. When they got there, the knight saw a boat. On it were many ladies in black.

"Put me in the boat," said the King. The ladies cried when they saw him. Then they rowed him away to the island of Avalon.

FOLK TALES FROM INDIA

THE TORTOISE WHO TALKED TOO MUCH

Once upon a time there was a Tortoise. He lived in a pond. He was a fine Tortoise. But he talked and talked! All day long, it was talk, talk—until the fish said they would rather live on dry land. They could not put up with it any more.

But the Tortoise had two friends—a pair of young Geese, who used to fly near the pond looking for food. They heard that everyone thought the Tortoise talked too much. So they flew up to him and said:

"Oh, Tortoise! Come along with us! We have such a beautiful home in the mountains. There you can talk all day long. Nobody will bother you there!"

"All very well," said the Tortoise. "But how am I to get there? I can't fly!"

"Oh, we'll carry you. But you must keep your mouth shut for a little while!"

"Yes, I can do that," he said, "when I want to. Let us be off."

So the Geese picked up a stick. One took one end in her bill. The other took the other end. Then they told the Tortoise to get hold in the middle. "Be careful," said they. "Do not talk."

The Tortoise held on to the stick with his teeth. He held on very tight! Then the Geese flapped their wings and flew toward home.

All went well for a time. But then some boys were looking up in the air. They thought a flying Tortoise was very funny.

"Look there!" cried one. "Two Geese carrying a Tortoise on a stick!"

The Tortoise heard this. And he was so angry that he forgot not to talk. He started to say: "What's that to you? Mind your own business!" But when he opened his mouth, he let go of the stick. Down he dropped. He fell with a crash on the stones.

Now the Tortoise was dead. His shell was cracked in two.

The Geese felt very sorry. "If only he had kept his mouth shut," they said.

THE CRANE AND THE CRAB

Once upon a time a lot of fish lived in a little pool. It was all very well while there was rain. But when summer came, it began to be very hot. The water dried up. It got lower and lower. Soon it was too hot for the fish.

Now not far away there was a beautiful lake. It was always fresh and cool. It had big trees around it. Water lilies covered it. (This kept it from drying up.) And a Crane lived on this lake.

The Crane used to eat fish, when he could catch any. One day the Crane came upon the little pool. He saw all the fish in it. Then he thought of a neat trick.

"Dear Fish," said the Crane, "I am so sorry to see you in this hole. I know a beautiful lake close by. It is deep and fresh and cool. If you like I will carry you there."

The Fish did not know what to make of this. Never since the world began had a Crane done a nice thing for a Fish. You see, it is silly to think a Crane would help a Fish. That is like a cat helping a mouse.

So they said to the Crane: "We don't believe you. You want to eat us."

But the Crane said, "No, no! I'm not as bad as all that. I have eaten a fish now and then. Yes, that's true. But I have plenty of other food. And it makes me sad to see you here. You will all be boiled before long!"

"That's true enough," said the Fish. "The water is hot." Well, in the end they talked an Old Fish into seeing how the lake was.

The Crane took the Old Fish in his beak. He put him in the lake. The Old Fish saw that what the Crane said was true. Then the Crane carried him back again to tell the others.

The Old Fish could not say enough about the lake. "It's ever so big," he said. "It is deep and cool. There are trees around. Water lilies are growing in the mud. There are also many fine fat flies! Ah, what a dinner I have had!"

Now all the Fish wanted to go. They came to the top of the water. "Please," they said, "please take us to the lake."

"One at a time!" said the Crane. "I have only one beak, you know!" And he smiled to himself. That beak was made to eat fish, not to carry them.

Now all the Fish said, "Old Fish, you have been very brave! You put yourself in the Crane's beak. It is only fair that you should go first."

So the Crane took the Old Fish in his beak. He carried him over to the lake. But this time he did not drop the Fish. He ate him up.

And so it went on. A few days later the pool was empty. The Crane had eaten every one of the fish! He stood on the bank, looking around. He wanted to see if there were any fish left. There had

to be one! But no, it was just a crab. Never mind, the Crane thought. A crab is as good as a fish.

So he asked the crab to come with him to the lake.

"Why, how are you going to carry me?" asked the Crab.

"In my beak," said the Crane.

"You might drop me," said the Crab, "and then I would break."

"Oh, no, I won't drop you!" said the Crane. But the Crab had more sense than all the fish put together. He did not believe the Crane at all. So he pretended to think. At last he said:

"Well, I'll tell you what. I can hold on tighter with my claws than you can with your beak. So you must let me hold on to your neck with my claws. Then I shall feel safe."

The Crane was very hungry. He did not stop to think. So he said yes. Then the Crab got hold of his neck with his claws. The Crane carried him toward the lake.

But after awhile the Crab saw that he

was not being carried to the lake! "Crane, dear," said he, "aren't you going to put me in the lake?"

"Crab, dear," said the Crane, "do you think I was born to carry crabs? Not I! Just look at that pile of bones under the tree! Those are the bones of the fish that used to live in your pool. I ate them. I'm going to eat you!"

"Are you, now?" said the crab. He gave the Crane's neck a little nip.

Then the Crane saw what a fool he had been! The Crab could kill him if he liked. Now he was afraid! And that is what happened to the Crane.

"Dear Crab!" said he. Tears were in his eyes. "I'm sorry! I won't kill you. Just let me go!"

"Put me in the lake, then," said the Crab.

The Crane went to the lake. And the Crab—as soon as he was safe—nipped off the Crane's head as clean as if it had been cut with a knife.

So the Crane was caught by his own trick. And the Crab lived happily in the beautiful lake for the rest of his life.

THE PIOUS WOLF

Once there was a flood. And there was a large rock with a Wolf sleeping on the top. The water came up around the rock. When the Wolf woke up he was trapped. He had no way to get off. There was nothing to eat.

"Hm!" said he to himself. "Here I am stuck! And here I shall have to stay for a while. Nothing to eat, either! Well," he thought, "today is Friday. Some people fast on Friday. Suppose I keep a holy fast today? A good idea!" So he crossed his paws, and pretended to pray. He thought he was very good to be fasting.

A fairy saw this. She heard what he said. So she thought she would just see how good the Wolf really was. So she changed herself into a goat. Then she jumped down out of the air on to the rock.

The Wolf opened an eye. There was a tender nice little goat. He forgot his prayer in a minute. "Aha!" said he. "A goat! I can keep my Friday fast tomorrow. Now for the goat!" He licked his lips, and jumped at the goat.

But the goat jumped away. Try as he would, he could not come near it. You know it was the fairy. And the fairy did not let herself be caught.

After trying to catch the goat for some time, the Wolf lay down again. "After all," said he, "it is Friday. I had best keep my fast today."

"You humbug!" said the fairy. Now she looked like herself again. "You pretend you are keeping a fast! You fast because you can't help it—not because you are really good. As a punishment, you shall stay on this rock till next Friday, and fast for a week!"

So saying, she opened her wings and flew far away.

UNCLE REMUS—TALES ABOUT ANIMALS

Uncle Remus is a group of tales about animals. It was written by Joel Chandler Harris (1848-1908). The adventures of Brer Rabbit, Brer Fox, and their friends are told to a little boy by his friend, Uncle Remus.

The author was born in the Southern state of Georgia. For many years he heard and remembered the wonderful stories told by the black people in Georgia. Then he retold them as Uncle Remus stories which also includes The Tar Baby, Uncle Remus and Brer Rabbit *and* Uncle Remus and the Little Boy.

A Story About the Little Rabbits

"Find them where you will," said Uncle Remus. "Good children always get taken care of! Like Brer Rabbit's children. They minded their daddy and mammy from day's end to day's end. When old man Rabbit said Scoot, they scooted. When old Miss Rabbit said Scat, they scatted. They did that. And they kept their clothes clean. They didn't have any dirt on their noses, either."

The little boy rubbed the end of his nose with his sleeve.

"They were good children," said the old man. "If they hadn't been, there was one time when there wouldn't have been any little Rabbits—not one! That's what."

"What time was that, Uncle Remus?" the little boy asked.

"The time when Brer Fox dropped in at Brer Rabbit's house, and didn't find anybody there except the little Rabbits. Old Brer Rabbit was off somewhere in a cabbage patch. Old Miss Rabbit was away working on a quilt. The little Rabbits were playing hide-and-seek. And in dropped Brer Fox! The little Rabbits were so fat that they made his mouth water. But he remembered about Brer Wolf. And he was afraid to eat them up without an excuse. The little Rabbits, they were mighty afraid. They sort of stuck together and watched Brer Fox. Brer Fox, he sat there. He studied what sort of an excuse he was going to make up. By and by he saw a big stalk of sugarcane in the corner. He cleared his throat and began to talk mighty big:

" 'Here! You young Rabbits there! Break me a piece off the sweet tree,' said he."

"The little Rabbits, they got out the sugarcane. They did. They pulled it and pushed it. But it was no use. They couldn't break it. Brer Fox, he made like he wasn't looking. Then he said, 'Hurry up there, Rabbits! I'm waiting on you.' "

"And the little Rabbits tried some more. But they couldn't break it. By and by they heard a little bird singing on top of the house. The song that the little bird sang was this:

> 'Take yo' toofies en gnaw it
> Take yo' toofies en saw it,
>   Saw it en yoke it,
> En den you kin broke it.'

Then the little Rabbits, they got mighty glad. They gnawed the cane through before old Brer Fox could say

anything more. They carried him the cane. Brer Fox, he sat there. He studied how he was going to make some other excuse for nabbing them. By and by he got down the sifter that was hanging on the wall, and he said:

" 'Come here, Rabbits! Take this sifter, and run down to the river. Get me some fresh water.' "

"The little Rabbits, they ran down to the spring. They tried to dip up the water with the sifter. But it all ran out. And it kept on running out. Well, by and by the little Rabbits sat down and began to cry. Then the little bird sitting up in the tree he began to sing, and this is the song that he sang:

'Sifter hold water same ez a tray,
Ef you fill it wid moss en dob
  it wid clay;
De Fox git madder de longer you
  stay—
Fill it wid moss en dob it wid clay.'

"Up they jumped, the little Rabbits did. They fixed the sifter so it wouldn't leak. Then they carried the water to old Brer Fox. Then Brer Fox he got mighty mad. He saw a great big stick of wood. 'Put that on the fire,' he said to the little ones. So they got around the wood, they did. They lifted it so hard. But the wood didn't move. Then they heard the little bird singing, and this is the song that he sang:

'Spit in yo' han's en tug it en
  toll it,
En git behine it, en push it, en
  pole it;
Spit in yo' han's en r'ar back and
  roll it.'

"And just about the time they got the wood on the fire, their daddy, he came skipping in. The little bird, he flew away. Brer Fox, he saw that his game was up. And it wasn't long before he made his excuses and started to go."

" 'You better stay. Take a snack with me, Brer Fox,' said Brer Rabbit, said he. 'Since Brer Wolf quit coming and sitting up with me, I am getting so I feel right lonesome these long nights,' said he."

"But Brer Fox, he buttoned up his coat. He just went off home. And that is what you'd better do, honey, because I see Miss Sally in front of the window. The first thing you know, she'll be expecting you."

The Story of the Flood And How It Came About

"One time," said Uncle Remus—"one time, way back. One time before you were born, honey. And before Master John or Miss Sally were born—way back before any of us were born, the animals talked among themselves. Then they had a meeting." The young boy looked surprised.

So Uncle Remus said, "In those days animals had a lot more sense than they have now. They had sense the same as folks. And when they made up their minds, it wasn't more than said before it was done. Well, they said they had to hold a meeting. They wanted to straighten out matters. Everyone was going to have a say. So when the day came they were on hand. The Lion, he was there, because he was the king. He had to be there. The Rhinoceros, he was there. The Elephant, he was there. The Camels, and the Cows, and down to the Crawfishes, they were there. They were all there. The Lion shook his head. He took his seat in the big chair. Then the meeting began.

"What did they do, Uncle Remus?" asked the little boy.

"I can't really remember what they did do. But they spoke. They yelled. By and by, they were fighting with one another. And the Elephant stepped on one of the Crawfishes. Of course when that animal puts his foot down, whoever is under there's bound to be squashed. And there wasn't enough of that Crawfish left to tell that he'd been there.

"This made the other Crawfishes mighty mad. They sort of got together and said they were going to war. But nobody heard it, except maybe the Mud Turtle and the Spring Lizard. No one listened to them either.

"By and by, the monkey was fighting with the Lion. The Hyena was laughing to himself. And the Elephant stepped on another one of the Crawfishes. In a little moment he would have stepped on the Mud Turtle too. Then the Crawfishes, what there was left of them, got together. They said that this time they meant it! They were going to war. But they might as well have been singing in a hurricane. The other animals were too busy fighting to hear them. So there they were, the Crawfishes. And they didn't know which of them was going to be next. And they kept on getting madder and madder. They got scareder and scareder too. Then by and by they began to make little holes in the ground. Soon they were out of sight."

"Who was, Uncle Remus?" asked the little boy.

"The Crawfishes, honey. They made holes in the ground. And they kept on going until they hit the rivers under the earth. The waters squirted out. They rose higher and higher until the hills were covered. The animals were all drowned. And all because they thought they were bigger than the Crawfishes."

Then the old man blew the ashes from a smoking yam.

"Where was the ark, Uncle Remus?" the little boy asked.

"Which ark is that?" asked the old man. He pretended he didn't know.

"Noah's ark," said the child.

"Don't you pester with old man Noah, honey. He took care of that ark. That's what he was there for, and that's what he done. At least that's what they tell me. But don't you bother about that ark. There might have been two floods. And then there might not have been. If there was any ark in this flood, I haven't heard tell of it. And when there aren't any arks around, I haven't got any time to make them up and put them in there. It's getting your bedtime, honey."

Mr. Rabbit Nibbles Up the Butter

"The animals," said Uncle Remus, shaking his coffee around the bottom of his tin cup, "they kept getting to know each other more and more. Until by and by, it wasn't long before Brer Rabbit, and Brer Fox, and Brer Possum got to sort of living together in the same forest. After a while the roof sort of began to leak. And one day, Brer Rabbit, and Brer Fox, and Brer Possum thought maybe they could fix it. They had a big day's work in front of them. So they got their dinner ready. Then they put the food in one pile, with the butter that Brer Fox brought. Then they went and put it all in the springhouse to keep them cool. And then they went to work. And it wasn't long before Brer Rabbit's stomach began to growl and pester him. That butter of Brer Fox's sat on his mind. His mouth watered every time he thought about it. Soon he said to himself that he would be pleased to have a bit of that butter. Then he laid his plans, he did. First, he raised his head quick and hollered out:

" 'Here I am. What do you want with me?' He ran off like something was after him.

"Then he waited around, old Brer Rabbit did. He made sure that nobody was following him. He went into the springhouse and got a bite of the butter. Then he came on back to work.

" 'Where've you been?' said Brer Fox.

" 'I heard my children calling me,' said Brer Rabbit. 'And I had to go and see what they wanted. My old wife had gone and taken sick,' said he.

"They worked on. By and by the butter tasted so good that old Brer Rabbit wanted some more. Then he raised up his head, he did, and hollered out:

" 'Heyo! Hold on! I'm a-coming!' and off he ran.

"This time he stayed a long while. When he got back Brer Fox asked him where he had been.

" 'I've been to see my old wife. She's not doing well,' he said.

"Then Brer Rabbit heard her calling him again. Off he went. This time, bless your soul, he ate so much butter he could see the bottom of the bucket! He scraped it clean. Licked it dry. Then he got back to work.

" 'How's your old wife this time?' said Brer Fox.

" 'Thank you for asking, Brer Fox,' said Brer Rabbit, 'but I'm afraid she's done gone by now.' And that sort of made Brer Fox and Brer Possum feel bad, along with Brer Rabbit.

"By and by, dinner-time came. They all got out the food. But Brer Rabbit kept on looking lonesome. Brer Fox and Brer Possum they sort of ran round to see if they couldn't make Brer Rabbit slimmy."

"What is that, Uncle Remus?" asked the little boy.

"Sort of splimmy-splammy, honey. Sort of like he was in a crowd. Sort of like his old wife wasn't dead. You know how folks do when someone's sad."

The little boy didn't know, but Uncle Remus went on:

"Brer Fox and Brer Possum rustled around, they did. They got out the food, and by and by Brer Fox, he said:

" 'Brer Possum, you run down to the spring. Get the butter. I'll go around here and set the table,' " he said.

"Brer Possum, he went off after the butter. Soon he came back with his tongue hanging out. Brer Fox hollered out:

" 'What's the matter now, Brer Possum?' said he.

" 'You all better run there, folks,' said Brer Possum, 'the last drop of that butter has gone!'

" 'Where's she gone?' said Brer Fox.

" 'Looks like she dried up,' said Brer Possum.

"Then Brer Rabbit, he look sort of sad he did. And he up and said:

" 'I expect that butter melted in somebody's mouth,' said he.

"Then they went down to the spring with Brer Possum. And sure enough the butter was gone. While they were thinking about it, Brer Rabbit said he saw tracks all round. He said, 'Let's all go to sleep. Then we can catch the chap that stole the butter.' So they all lay down. Brer Fox and Brer Possum they soon dropped off to sleep. But Brer Rabbit he stayed awake. When the time came he put butter on Brer Possum's mouth. Then he ran off. He ate up the best of the dinner that they left lying out. Then he came back. He woke up Brer Fox and showed him the butter on Brer Possum's mouth. Then they woke up Brer Possum and told him about it. Brer Possum said he didn't do it. But looked at it this way—Brer Possum was the first one at the butter. He was the first one to miss it. And more than that, there was butter on his mouth. Brer Possum saw that they had him in a corner. So he up and said that the way to catch the man that stole the butter was to build a big brush-heap. Set her afire, and all hands try to jump over it. The one that fell in was the one who stole the butter. Brer Rabbit and Brer Fox they both said yes, they did. And they built the brush-heap. They built her high and they built her wide. Then they set her on fire. When she got to burning good, Brer Rabbit, he took the first turn. He sort of stepped back. He looked around and laughed. Over he went like a bird flying. Then came Brer Fox. He got back a little

further. He spit on his hands, and made the jump. But he came very near getting in that the end of his tail caught fire. Haven't you ever seen a fox, honey?" asked Uncle Remus.

The little boy thought probably he had. But he wouldn't say.

"Well, then," said the old man, "next time you see one of them, you look right close. See if the end of his tail isn't white. It's just like I told you. That's what the fire did. Burned his tail, it did. It shows right to this day. Right to this day."

"And what about Brother Possum?" asked the little boy.

"Old Brer Possum, he took a running start, he did. He came along, and he lit—kerblam!—right in the middle of the fire. And that was the last of old Brer Possum."

"But Uncle Remus, Brother Possum didn't steal the butter!" said the little boy.

"That's what makes me say what I do, honey. In this world, lots of folks have to pay for other folks' sins. Looks like it's mighty wrong. But it's just that way, honey."

Mr. Terrapin Shows His Strength

"Brer Terrapin was a smart man," said Uncle Remus, rubbing his hands together. "He was the smartest man of the whole gang. He was that."

The little boy sat very still. Uncle Remus looked in one pocket and then another. Then he filled his pipe. Soon the old man went on.

"One night Miss Meadows began a candy-pulling. So many friends came she had to put the molasses in the washpot.

She had to build the fire in the yard.
Now Brer Bear, he helped Miss
Meadows bring the wood. Brer Fox, he
minded the fire. Brer Wolf, he kept the
dogs off. Brer Rabbit, he greased the
plates to keep the candy from sticking.
And Brer Terrapin, he climbed up in a
chair. He said he'd watch and see that
the molasses didn't boil over. They were
all there. And they weren't cutting up
either. Miss Meadows, she put her foot
down, she did. She said that when they
came to her place they had to be good.

"Well, then, they were all sitting
there. And the molasses was boiling.
And they got to talking mighty big. Brer
Rabbit, he said he was the fastest. But
Brer Terrapin, he rocked for a long time
and watched the molasses. Brer Fox, he
said he was the sharpest. But Brer Terrapin, he kept on rocking. Brer Wolf, he
said he was the most crafty. But Brer

Terrapin, he rocked and he rocked. Brer
Bear, he said he was the strongest. But
Brer Terrapin, he rocked, and he kept on
rocking. By and by, he sort of shut one
eye, and he said,

" 'It looks I'm not much of anything.
Yet here I am. And I can show Brer
Rabbit that he isn't the fastest. And I
can show Brer Bear that he isn't the
strongest,' said he.

"Then they all laughed because it
looked like Brer Bear was stronger than
a steer. By and by, Miss Meadows, she
up and asked how he was going to do it.

" 'Give me a good strong rope,' said
Brer Terrapin. 'Let me get in a puddle of
water. Then let Brer Bear see if he can
pull me out,' " said he.

"Then they all laughed again. Brer
Bear, he up and said, 'We haven't got a
rope,' said he.

" 'No,' said Brer Terrapin, 'and have

you got the strength either.' Then Brer Terrapin, he rocked and rocked. He watched the molasses boiling.

"After a while, Miss Meadows, she up and said that she'd find a rope. And while the candy was cooling they could go to the creek.

"Now," said Uncle Remus, "Brer Terrapin wasn't much bigger than the palm of my hand. It looked mighty funny to hear him bragging about how he could outpull Brer Bear. But they got the rope. And they all put out for the creek. Brer Terrapin found the place he wanted. Then he took one end of the rope, and gave the other end to Brer Bear.

" 'Now then, said Brer Terrapin, 'you all go with Brer Bear up there in the woods. I'll stay here. When you hear me holler, then's the time for Brer Bear to pull. You all take care of that end,' said he, 'and I'll take care of this end.'

"Then they all left Brer Terrapin at the creek. When they got good and gone, he dove down into the water, he did. He tied the rope to one of the big clay roots. Then he came up and yelled, 'Pull!'

"Brer Bear wrapped the rope round his hand. He winked at everyone. With that he gave a big jerk, but Brer Terrapin didn't move. Then he turned around, he did. He put the rope across his shoulders. He tried to walk off with Brer Terrapin. But Brer Terrapin looked like he didn't feel like walking. Then Brer Wolf helped Brer Bear pull. But it was just like he didn't. Then they all helped him. And my! my! while they were all pulling, Brer Terrapin asked them when they were going to start. Then when Brer Terrapin felt them quit pulling, he dove down, he did. He untied the rope. By the time they got to the creek, Brer Terrapin, he was sitting at the edge of the water. He up and said, said he:

" 'That last pull of yours was good. A little more and you would have had me,' said he. 'You're good, Brer Bear,' said he, 'and you pull hard. But I guess I sort of got the better of you,' said he.

"Then Brer Bear, he up and said he'd like to see if the candy was ready. And off they went after it."

"It's a wonder," said the little boy, "that the rope didn't break."

"Break who?" said Uncle Remus, "break who? In those days, Miss Meadows's rope would haul a mule."

This put an end to whatever doubts the child might have had.

ROBIN HOOD AND HIS MERRY MEN

Tales of Robin Hood have been told for many years. He was an outlaw. People think he lived about 800 years ago.

During that time King Richard I was King of England. But he spent many years away, fighting in another Land. While he was gone his brother John ruled.

It is said that John was a bad King. Robin Hood was against him. He and his band of men tried to help the poor people.

Nobody knows if there ever really was a man called Robin Hood. But the songs and stories about him have made him one of the heroes of England.

Brave and Merry Men

Robin Hood led a band of brave and merry men. They lived in Sherwood Forest near Nottingham. One of the most famous was Little John. He was given his name in fun. He really was very big and strong. Robin's priest was a fat, jolly man called Friar Tuck. Other men in his band were Will Scarlet, Arthur-a-Bland, Will Stutly, Much, the miller's son, and the minstrel, Allen-a-Dale.

Dressed in green, these bold men hunted the King's deer. They were very good with bows and arrows. They also robbed people on the highway. But they robbed the rich to give to the poor.

Robin was also good at war. But he didn't kill if he could help it. He would rob the rich, he said. But he would be nice to them. He just wanted their gold.

Robin's name was known all over the land. People he had robbed told stories of how they were carried into Sherwood Forest. They were given a dinner good enough for a king. They paid for their dinner with gold. Then they were sent on their way.

Robin's greatest enemy was the Sheriff of Nottingham. Robin loved to make fun of him. And he was always trying to catch Robin and his men.

The outlaws took a lot of chances. Once Little John became a servant in the sheriff's house. While there, he played tricks on another servant. At last he knocked him over and ran off to the forest with the sheriff's silver plate.

One day the sheriff said there would be an archery contest. He hoped that Robin Hood would come to take part. Then he could catch him. But Robin went in a disguise. He won the top prize, which was given to him by the sheriff! After Robin Hood was back in the forest, the sheriff learned of the trick that had been played on him.

Robin and Maid Marian

One fine day Robin Hood rode through the forest. He had not gone far when he came upon a knight. The knight and Robin fought. After some minutes the knight was hurt. Robin took off the knight's helmet. To his surprise, he saw that the "knight" was a girl—Maid Marian.

Now Maid Marian was the daughter of

an Earl. She and Robin had been sweethearts before Robin had become an outlaw.

Robin could have cried at hurting her. But he saw that Maid Marian was not cut badly. In fact she had come to look for him. He blew on his horn to call his men together.

Robin's men came from every part of the forest. When they heard Marian's story they said they would serve her. Friar Tuck married Robin and Marian there in the forest.

The Bishop of Hereford

The Bishop of Hereford was another of Robin's enemies. One summer day he rode into the forest with soldiers. He hoped to catch Robin. Then he would take him to the Sheriff of Nottingham. As luck would have it, Robin was alone in the forest that day.

The bishop's men saw him before he saw them. They charged down on him. Robin took to his heels. He ran behind trees. He ran in ditches. The horses of the soldiers tripped. They threw many of their riders to the ground.

Robin ran hard till he reached the cottage of a poor old woman. He asked her to hide him. But the old woman knew there was nowhere in the house where he would be safe. She told him to put on her jacket and dress. She tied her shawl round his head. Then she put on Robin's clothes and hid herself. Robin sat down at the spinning wheel and began to work.

When the soldiers came, they looked at the woman. They told her to show them where she had hidden Robin Hood. But the old woman kept on working. She talked to herself. She kept her head over the wheel. The soldiers thought she was an idiot. So they began to look around the cottage. When they came to the cupboard, they found the old woman in Robin's clothes. With the cap drawn over her face she looked very much like Robin Hood.

The soldiers were very happy. They had found Robin Hood! They carried him out of the cottage and put him on a horse. Then the bishop, the soldiers and the old woman went to Nottingham.

Robin ran from the cottage into the forest. He called his men together. Quickly he told them what had happened.

The bishop's party went through the forest. Suddenly there were Robin and his men. The soldiers laid down their arms. The old woman was let go. And the bishop had to give up all his money.

"It belongs to the church," said the bishop.

"No," said Robin. "It belongs to the poor. You took it from them. Now they will get it back."

Robin Hood's Last Days

The years passed and Robin grew very weak. He had an old wound that would not heal. He said he would go and visit Lady Ursula to see if she could cure him. Little John was very sad because his master was so sick. So he took him there.

The Lady would not let Little John take care of Robin Hood. She sent him away.

Now Lady Ursula was a greedy woman. She was not a real friend. An old enemy of Robin's came to her. He said he would give her land and gold if she would kill Robin.

So the Lady worked out a way to kill Robin. When she tied up his wound she tied it too tightly. Robin became very faint.

He took his horn which lay by the bed. With it he called his friend Little John to his side. He told Little John he was dying. He asked him to give him his bow and arrow. Then he shot an arrow through the window. Robin told Little John that he would be buried where the arrow fell.

Lay me a green sod under my head,
  And another at my feet,
And lay my bent bow by my side,
  Which was my music sweet;
And make my grave of gravel and
  green,
  Which is most right and meet.
Let me have length and breadth
  enough,
  With a green sod at my head,
That they may say when I am dead:
  "Here lies bold Robin Hood."

THE REAL PRINCESS

There was once a young Prince. He said "I want to marry a *real* Princess."

So he went all over the world to find one. He did meet many. But he could never be sure that they were *real* Princesses.

At last he had to come home again. "A real Princess," he said "is hard to find.

But I am sure she would be more delicate than other people."

One night there was a bad storm. The thunder crashed. The lightning flashed. It rained and rained. Just when the storm was at its worst, there was a knock. The old King himself went down to answer it.

A young girl stood outside. The wind had almost blown her away. Water ran from her hair and her clothes. Her feet were very wet.

"Who are you?" asked the King. "And why are you out on such a night?"

"I am a Princess," she said. "A *real* Princess. I have lost my way. I am looking for somewhere to stay."

Now the Queen heard the Princess say she was a real Princess.

"Well, we shall find out if you are!" thought the Queen. Then she made a plan. She went into the bedroom, and put a small dried pea on the bed. Then she put five mattresses on top of the pea. On top of these she put five feather beds. She helped the princess to climb up on top.

When the Princess came down the next morning, the Queen asked how she had slept.

"Not well!" said the Princess. "I am sure there was a large stone in my bed. I only slept for a few minutes the whole night!"

The Queen still was not sure the Princess was a *real* Princess. So she wanted to try the plan again. That night she went to the bedroom. She put twenty mattresses on top of the pea. On top of these she put twenty feather beds. She asked for a ladder. And the Princess climbed up on top to sleep.

In the morning she asked her how she had slept.

"It was very bad!" said the Princess.

"I was awake the whole night long! There was something in my bed. It felt like a rock. Now I am black and blue all over!"

So then they knew that she was a real Princess. Even with twenty mattresses and the twenty feather beds, she had still felt the pea. No one but a real Princess could have such a tender skin.

This made the Prince want her for his wife. They both lived happily for the rest of their lives. As for the pea, it was put in a museum where it still is—if no one has carried it away.

JOHNNY APPLESEED

In the early days of America, there was a man called John Chapman. He was a very special man. And he felt he had a special job to do. He wanted to plant apple trees all over the country.

So every year when the cider was made, he would wash the apple seeds. Then he let them dry in the sun. He loved to run his fingers over the smooth seeds.

The next spring, he would put some of the seeds into sacks. Then he walked west. He would give the little sacks to families who were moving west. The big sacks he carried to use himself. Here and there he planted the seeds—along the

rivers and in the fields. Even after the seeds had begun to grow, Johnny Appleseed (as he was called by now) would return to care for the young trees.

Over the years, Johnny walked thousands of miles. He slept out in the open. He went through mud and snow. He walked as far south as Tennessee and as far west as the Rocky Mountains.

Some people thought he was very silly. They could not understand why Johnny Appleseed worked so hard. He did not get anything in return! But Johnny didn't care. He would plant trees and look after them for any family who would let him. And he traveled alone. He did not have a knife or a gun to protect him from the wild animals and Indians. He was not afraid. In fact he became great friends with the Indians. And he believed that the animals would not hurt him.

"Leave animals alone," he would say, "and they'll do the same by you."

SINBAD THE SAILOR

One day Sinbad the Sailor heard a man say: "Life is not fair. I have worked harder than Sinbad. Yet he lives well and I am poor."

"Hear what I went through to get my money! Then you will feel better," said Sinbad.

"Look at my white hair! I seem to be an old man. But I was young and strong the day I went away. Soon after we left, there was no wind. Our ship was near a little island. So we went ashore to look about. But what we thought was an island was the back of a great whale.

"As soon as we landed it began to move. Then it went under the waves.

We were left in the sea. I hung on to a piece of wood. Then I was washed up on an island.

"After a few days, I found some fruit trees. In the middle was a great white ball the size of a house. I ate some of the fruit. Then I lay down near the ball to sleep. Just as I was closing my eyes I looked up. The sky was dark. A giant bird was above me.

" 'Good heavens!' I said. 'This great white ball is the egg of that monster bird called a roc.'

"I was very afraid. The roc sat on the egg. One of its claws was as big as a tree. It stuck into my clothes.

"When day came, the roc flew up into the air. It carried me so high I could not see the earth. After flying about it came toward the earth again. It went so fast, I nearly lost my mind. When it was on the ground I pulled my clothes from its claws. Now I was in a deep valley. There were big mountains on every side.

"I looked around. What I saw was so beautiful! I could not believe my eyes! The ground was covered with jewels. It was the Valley of the Diamonds that I had heard people talk of! Full of joy, I began to fill my pockets. I took as many as I could carry. But soon I was very afraid. The valley was also full of great snakes.

"I went into a cave to hide. All night I could hear the snakes. In the morning they left. They were afraid of the roc. It

would come back to look for food. I came out of the cave. Then I was knocked down by something. It was a great piece of fresh meat that rolled down the mountain. As it rolled the diamonds stuck to it. I saw a lot of men who were throwing down another piece of meat.

"I tied myself to the meat. Then I hid under it. Soon an eagle picked up the meat and carried it to the top of the mountains. The men drove the eagle away. They turned the meat over to pick off the diamonds and found me.

"When they had all the diamonds they wanted, we sailed for home. But we went by the island. The men landed. They took an ax and broke open the great white ball. A scream rang through the sky. The roc had seen them. They ran back to the ship, and we set sail. But we were followed by the roc. It was holding a big rock. Then it dropped this on our ship.

Down we all went into the sea. I held on to a piece of wood with one hand, and with the other I swam to another island.

"It was a nice spot. Full of streams and fruit. There I met some sailors. I came home with them.

"Now don't you think," said Sinbad "that I have earned all that I took from the Valley of the Diamonds?"

The man said that he did. And Sinbad gave him a present. Then the man went home and felt better about his own life.

STORIES TO READ ALOUD

HENNY-PENNY

Once upon a time there was a silly hen. Her name was Henny-Penny.

One day Henny-Penny was walking through the woods. Whack! A nut hit her on the head. She did not know what it was. And she thought the sky was falling! "My, my!" said Henny-Penny. "I must go and tell the king. The sky is falling in."

So she went along. And she went along. Then she met Cocky-Locky.

"Where are you going?" asked Cocky-Locky.

"O-oh! I am going to tell the king that the sky is falling in," said Henny-Penny.

"May I come with you?" asked Cocky-Locky.

"Oh, yes!" said Henny-Penny.

So Henny-Penny and Cocky-Locky went along. And they went along. Then they met Ducky-Lucky.

"Where are you going?" asked Ducky-Lucky.

"Oh, I met Henny-Penny," said Cocky-Locky. "She said the sky is falling in. So we are going to tell the king."

"May I come too?" asked Ducky-Lucky.

"Oh, yes!" said Henny-Penny and Cocky-Locky.

So Henny-Penny and Cocky-Locky and Ducky-Lucky went along. They went along. Then they met Goosey-Poosey.

"Where are you going?" asked Goosey-Poosey.

"Oh, I met Cocky-Locky," said Ducky-Lucky, "He met Henny-Penny. She said that the sky is falling in. So we are going to tell the king."

"May I come too?" asked Goosey-Poosey.

"Oh, yes," said Henny-Penny and Cocky-Locky and Ducky-Lucky.

So Henny-Penny and Cocky-Locky and Ducky-Lucky and Goosey-Poosey went along. They went along. Then they met Turkey-Lurkey.

"Where are you going?" asked Turkey-Lurkey.

"Oh, I met Ducky-Lucky," said Goosey-Poosey. "She met Cocky-Locky. He met Henny-Penny. And she said the sky is falling in. So we are going to tell the king."

"May I come too?" asked Turkey-Lurkey.

"Oh, yes," said Henny-Penny and Cocky-Locky and Ducky-Lucky and Goosey-Poosey and Turkey-Lurkey. They went along. They went along. Then they met Foxy-Woxy.

"Where are you going?" asked Foxy-Woxy.

"Oh, I met Goosey-Poosey," said Turkey-Lurkey. "She met Ducky-Lucky, and she met Cocky-Locky. And he met Henny-Penny. She said the sky is falling in. So we are going to tell the king."

"Well," said Foxy-Woxy, "you are all going the wrong way. This is not the way to reach the king. Come with me. I will show you the right road."

So Henny-Penny and Cocky-Locky and Ducky-Lucky and Goosey-Poosey and Turkey-Lurkey followed Foxy-Woxy.

They went along. They went along. They went along. Then they came to a big, dark hole.

"This is the way to the king," said Foxy-Woxy. "Follow me!"

Foxy-Woxy jumped down into the hole. Then in went Henny-Penny, Cocky-Locky, Ducky-Lucky, Goosey-Poosey and Turkey-Lurkey.

Now, Foxy-Woxy went right down to the bottom of that big, dark hole. He waited for the silly animals to follow him. Then Henny-Penny came down. Snap . . . snap went his sharp teeth. He tried to bite her head off. But it was very dark in the hole. So all he got was two of her feathers.

"Squawk, squawk!" cried Henny-Penny.

"Cock-a-doodle-doo!" cried Cocky-Locky.

"Quack, quack!" cried Ducky-Lucky.

"Quonk, quonk!" cried Goosey-Poosey.

"Gobble, gobble!" cried Turkey-Lurkey.

Then out of the big, dark hole came Henny-Penny, Cocky-Locky, Ducky-Lucky, Goosey-Poosey and Turkey-Lurkey. They ran along. They ran along. They ran along until they were as far away from Foxy-Woxy as they could get.

And they never did tell the king that the sky was falling in.

THE WOLF AND THE SEVEN KIDS

There was once an old goat who had seven kids. She loved them just as much as a mother loves her children. One day she was going into the woods. She wanted to get food for them. So she called them all to her, and said:

"My dear children, I am going out into the woods. Watch out for the wolf! If he gets into the house, he will eat you up—skin, and hair, and all. Remember, the wolf can put on different clothes. But

you will know him by his rough voice and his black feet."

The kids said: "Oh, we will be very careful mother. You may be quite happy about us."

So the old goat went off to her work. Before long, someone knocked at the door, and said:

"Open the door, dear children! Your mother has come back. She brought something for each of you."

But the kids knew quite well that it was the wolf!

"We won't open the door!" they said. "You are not our mother. She has a soft voice. But yours is rough. We know you are the wolf!"

So the wolf went away to a shop. He bought some chalk which he ate. It made his voice quite soft. Then he went back. He knocked at the door again and said:

"Open the door, dear children. Your mother has come back. She brought something for each of you."

But the wolf had put one of his paws on the window. The kids saw it, and said:

"We won't open the door. Our mother doesn't have a black foot. You are the wolf."

Then the wolf ran to a bakery. He bought some flour to whiten his paws. Now he went to the door. He knocked and said:

"Open the door, children. Your dear mother has come home. She has brought something for each of you out of the woods."

The kids said: "Show us your feet first. We want to be sure you are our mother."

The wolf put his paws on the window. The kids saw they were white. So they opened the door.

But it was the wolf who walked in! They were very afraid. They tried to hide. One ran under the table. The second jumped into bed. The third ran into the oven. The fourth ran into the kitchen. The fifth got into the closet. The sixth got into the washtub. The seventh hid in the tall clock. But the wolf found them all. All but one. He couldn't find the youngest one in the clock. So he ate the six, one after the other. Then he left the house. He lay down in a field outside.

Soon he fell asleep. Not long after, the old nanny-goat came back from the woods. Oh, how the house looked! The door was wide open. The table and chairs were turned over. The bowl was broken. The covers and pillows were on the floor. She looked all over the house for her children. But she could not find them. She called them by name, one by one. No one answered. At last, when she came to the youngest, a little voice said:

"I am here, dear mother. In the clock."

She brought him out. He told her the wolf had come and eaten all the others.

You can picture how she cried over her children!

At last, she could not look at the poor house anymore. So she went out. The youngest kid ran by her side. When they went into the field, they saw the wolf under a tree. He was snoring very loudly. They looked at him from every side. The could see something moving in his stomach.

"Ah, heavens!" thought the goat, "are my poor children still alive?"

She sent the kid running to the house. "Get me a scissors, needles, and thread," she said. Then she cut a hole in the wolf's side. Soon a kid popped out its head. When the hole was big enough, all six jumped out one after the other—all alive! And they were fine. The wolf was so hungry he had swallowed them whole. The mother was so happy. She hugged them. She danced around. At last she said:

"Go and get some big stones, children. We will fill up the hungry wolf while he is asleep."

Then the seven kids brought a lot of stones. They stuffed the wolf. The old mother sewed him up.

At last, the wolf had had his sleep. He got up and found he was very thirsty. He wanted to go to the river to drink. But as soon as he began to move, the stones began to roll about in his body. He said:

"What rattles, what rattles
Against my poor bones?
Surely not little goats,
But only big stones!"

And when he came to the river he bent over to drink. The heavy stones made him lose his balance. So he fell, and sank in the water.

The seven little goats saw this. They came running up, singing "The wolf is dead! The wolf is dead!" They danced for joy around their mother.

ALADDIN AND HIS WONDERFUL LAMP

A magician once went from Africa to Persia. He wanted to find a wonderful lamp. To find it, he had to go to a cave under the earth. There would be great danger. But the magician did not want to risk his life. So he made friends ith a boy called Aladdin.

Aladdin's father had died. The boy lived alone with his mother. So the magician pretended to be the boy's long lost uncle. He went with Aladdin to his home. At first the mother did not believe this man. "How do I know you are the brother of my dead husband?" she said. But the magician had on fine clothes. He promised to set Aladdin up in a shop of his own. When she heard this, the mother gave the magician supper. She asked him to come again the next day.

The next day the magician called. He said that he would take Aladdin to spend the day in the country. He led Aladdin out of one of the city gates. He talked the whole time to stop him from being afraid. Then he took him to a place between two mountains.

"I think so much of you," the magician said, "I am going to show you some African magic. First you must get enough sticks and make a fire."

So Aladdin picked up dried sticks. When they were burning, the magician put his hands over the fire and said some magic words. Smoke rose up. The ground shook under their feet. The earth opened before them. And there was a great stone with a brass ring in it! Aladdin was afraid. He turned to run. But the magician knocked him down.

He said, "Only you can pick up this stone and take the treasure under it. So you must do what I say. Take the ring and lift up the stone."

"I am not strong enough to do that alone," said Aladdin.

"You must. If I help you, we shall not get the treasure," said the magician. "Take hold of the ring. You can move the stone easily."

Aladdin did as he was told. To his surprise he was able to pick up the stone. Under it there were stairs leading to a door.

"The door leads into a cave. The cave had three great halls," said the magician. "When you go through, wrap your robe about you. Do not stop or touch the walls—not even with your clothes, or you will die. Go to the end of the third hall. You will find a door. It opens into a garden of fruit trees. Walk across the garden to a terrace. There you will see a lamp. Put out the light. Throw away the oil. Then bring it to me."

The magician took a ring from his finger. He gave it to Aladdin and said: "This is a charm. It will help you as long as you do what I say. Now go. We will both be rich for the rest of our lives. Go, Aladdin."

Aladdin did as the magician said. He opened the door and found the three halls. He went through them. He crossed the garden. Then he found the lamp. He blew it out. He took out the oil. Then he started back. But as he crossed the garden he stopped to look at the trees. He had never seen such beautiful fruit. It was so hard and shiny. He did not know it, but the fruits were jewels. Aladdin put them in his pockets. Then he ran through the halls.

"Give me the lamp!" said the magician.

"As soon as I am up," said Aladdin.

"Give me the lamp!" said the magician again.

"As soon as I am up," said Aladdin. He thought his uncle was going to help him. But the magician was very angry. He said two magic words. The stone moved back into place. Aladdin was trapped under the earth. It was very, very dark.

Aladdin was very afraid. He went down to the door. He wanted to go back to the garden, but now the door was closed. Aladdin sat on the stairs. He rubbed his hands, trying to think of what to do. As he did so, he rubbed the ring the magician had given him. And a great genie stood before him. He said: "What do you want? I am ready to do what you say."

"Take me home!" said Aladdin. As soon as he spoke he was with his mother. He told her all that had happened. She was so happy to see her son!

But the next morning, Aladdin's mother said there was no food to eat. Aladdin gave her the lamp. He told her to sell it. Before she went out, she tried to clean it. As soon as she began to rub, a giant genie said in a loud voice, "What do you want?"

Aladdin grabbed the lamp. He said, "Bring us something to eat."

The genie disappeared. But he came back with a large tray. On it were meats, cakes, and fruit. Aladdin and his mother had a fine dinner. But his mother said, "Genies are devils. We must never use the lamp again."

Aladdin said nothing. But he hid the lamp.

For many years, Aladdin and his mother lived well with the help of the genie. Then one day, Aladdin was nineteen. He heard that the daughter of the Sultan would be carried through the streets. Aladdin wanted to see the princess. So he ran into the street. The moment he saw her he fell deeply in love with her.

Aladdin ran home. He took all the

jewels he had taken from the trees in the cave. "Mother," he said, "take these to the Sultan. Ask him to let me marry the princess."

Aladdin's mother took the jewels. The Sultan saw their beauty. He said Aladdin could marry the princess.

Aladdin and the princess lived happily for many years. But then one day the magician learned that Aladdin was alive and was using the lamp. He went to the city where Aladdin lived. When he got there Aladdin was away. So the magician thought of a plan to get the lamp away from the princess. He bought twelve copper lamps and put them in a basket. Then he went to Aladdin's home, crying, "New lamps for old! Who will give me old lamps for new?"

Some children followed him. They hooted at him and teased him. But he did not listen. He walked back and forth.

"New lamps for old!" he called. At last the princess sent a servant to find out what the old man wanted.

"He says he will give new lamps for old!" the servant said. "I do not know how he can be so silly."

Laughing, the princess remembered the old lamp. It was back in her husband's closet. She sent the servant to bring it. Then she turned it in for a new one. So the magician at last had the magic lamp. He ran out of the city with it. When he was alone he rubbed the lamp. He said, "Genie, take me back to Africa. I want the princess to go with me."

When Aladdin returned, he could not believe his eyes! Where was his home? Where was his wife? Where were his servants? Not only that but the Sultan blamed Aladdin because he could not find his daughter.

Aladdin ran away to the country. He walked about thinking for three days. Then he happened to rub the ring that the magician had given him many years before. The genie of the ring stood before him. He said, "What do you want?"

"Bring my wife back," said Aladdin.

But the genie said, "I cannot do that. I am the slave of the ring, not of the lamp."

"Then carry me to where she is now," said Aladdin.

Just then Aladdin found himself in Africa. He stood in front of his home. He went through its gates and found the princess. She was so very happy to see him. Aladdin hugged and kissed her. Then he said: "Tell me, what has become of my old lamp?"

Then the Princess told how she had turned the old lamp in for a new one. She said that the evil man had her in his power. He always carried that very lamp. Aladdin was then sure that this man was the magician.

He told the whole story to his wife. Then they hit upon a plan for getting the lamp back. Aladdin went into the city. He bought a certain powder. Then the princess asked the magician to eat with her. She was very kind to him. Then she handed him a cup of wine. The powder was mixed in it. He drank it, and fell down dead. Now Aladdin came out from where he was hiding. He took the lamp back from the magician. He rubbed it and told the genie to take them back to Persia.

At break of day, the Sultan saw his daughter again. He was so happy! He gave a great feast for Aladdin and made Aladdin his heir.

THE EMPEROR'S NEW CLOTHES

Many years ago there was an emperor. He liked new clothes so much that he spent all his money on them.

He did not care about his soldiers. He did not care about the hunt. All he liked to do was show off his new clothes. He had a different suit for each hour of the day.

One day, two men came to the city. They said they were tailors. And they told everyone that they knew how to make special cloth. "Our cloth has the most beautiful colors. It is the best in the land." They also said this cloth had wonderful power. Those who were unfit for the office, or who happened to be a fool, could not see it.

"This must be fine cloth!" thought the emperor when he heard the story. "I want a suit made out of it. Then I can find out what men are unfit for their office. I will also know who is a fool and who is not. Get me the cloth. Have the tailors make me a suit. At once!" said the Emperor.

And so the emperor gave a lot of money to the men. He wanted them to begin their work right away.

The two men set up two looms. They pretended to work very hard. But they really did nothing at all. They asked for the best silk and gold thread. Then they put both into their own sacks. They pretended to work until late at night.

"I want to know how the men are getting on with my cloth," the emperor said, after a while.

But he was embarrassed when he remembered—only a fool could not see the cloth.

"I will send my minister to see," said the emperor at last. "He will be able to tell how the cloth looks. There is no one more fit for his office than he!"

So the minister went into the hall. The men seemed to be working at empty looms.

"What can this mean?" thought the old man. He opened his eyes very wide. "I cannot see any cloth!" But he did not say anything.

The men asked him to come near. "Aren't the colors beautiful?" they asked.

The poor old minister looked and looked. But he could not see anything. There was nothing there to see!

He thought "What! Am I a fool? I have never thought so. And if I am, no one must know. Can it be that I am not fit for my office? No, that can not be said either. I cannot say that I could not see the cloth."

"Well, sir minister," said one of the men, "you haven't said if you like the cloth."

"Oh, it is beautiful," said the old minister. "These colors—I will tell the emperor how very beautiful I think they are!"

"Thank you very much," said the men. Then they named the different colors. They talked about the patterns. Then they asked for more silk and gold. "We must have more," they said, "or else we will never get done." Soon the silk and gold were given to them. They put it into their sack. Then they pretended to go back to work.

The emperor now sent another person

to see how the men were getting on. He wanted to know if the cloth would soon be ready. It was just the same with this man as with the minister. He looked at the looms on all sides. But he couldn't see anything!

"I am not a fool!" thought the man. "It must be that I am not fit for my office! That is very odd! I can't tell anyone about it." And so he said he loved the cloth he could not see. He said the colors and patterns were beautiful.

"Yes," he said to his emperor when he returned, "the cloth is the most beautiful I have ever seen!"

And now the emperor wanted to see the cloth for himself.

So he took a few officers of the court and he went to see the two men. As soon as they knew the emperor was coming, they started working harder than ever.

"Isn't the cloth beautiful?" said the two officials who had been to the looms. "Look at it! What a great design! What pretty colors!" And at the same time, they pointed to the empty frames. They thought that everyone but themselves could see the cloth.

"How is this?" said the emperor to himself. "I can't see anything. Am I a fool? Am I unfit to be an emperor? That would be the worst thing that could happen . . ."

He looked at his officers. "Oh, the cloth is beautiful!" he said. There was no way he could say he couldn't see the cloth.

Now all the officers looked. They all hoped to see something. But it was no use! Yet they all said, "Oh, how beautiful!" And they told the emperor to have some new clothes. "You can wear them in the parade," they said.

The two men sat up the whole night

before the parade. They left all the lights on, so that everyone could see how hard they were working. The next day, they came to the palace with big boxes. They bowed before the emperor. "Please, sir, have your clothes taken off. We will put on your new clothes in front of the mirror."

The emperor took off his clothes. The two men pretended to dress him in the new suit. The emperor turned around and round in front of the mirror.

"How great the emperor looks in his new clothes! How well they fit!" everyone cried out. "What colors! Oh my, they are beautiful!"

The emperor turned around in front of the mirror again. "I am quite ready," he said. "Do my new clothes fit well?" he asked. No one dared say that they knew the emperor was quite naked.

The lords, who were to carry the emperor's train, felt around on the ground. But there was nothing to pick up. So they pretended they were carrying the ends of the train. They didn't want to be fools or unfit for office!

So now the emperor walked in the parade. He went through the streets of the city. All the people standing by said:

"Oh, how beautiful are our emperor's new clothes! What a great train! What beautiful colors! We have never seen clothes like these!"

"But the emperor has nothing on!" said a little child.

"Oh, my!" the father laughed. "You silly child." But what the child said was whispered from one person to another.

"But he has nothing on!" cried out all the people.

The emperor was upset. He knew the people were right. And, at last, he said to himself. "I really am not fit for my office! I am going to give up all the silly things I do and rule my country well!"

The two men were afraid they would be punished. So they ran away and were forgotten. The emperor and his people lived happily for many years.

JACK THE GIANT-KILLER

Long ago there lived a farmer's son named Jack. Not far away from Jack's home was a cave. In it lived a horrible giant. He was called Cormoran!

Cormoran was three times as big as any other man. His appetite was very big. So he stole all the sheep and oxen he could find. For one meal the giant could eat six oxen and twelve sheep.

Jack's father said, "This can't go on! He's eating all our animals. We won't have any left."

This set Jack thinking. Then he made up his mind. He was going to kill the giant.

So one night Jack set out for the giant's cave. With a spade he dug a deep pit. Then he covered it with sticks and stones until it looked like the earth around it. Now he was ready! He blew his cow-horn.

The giant jumped out of bed. He was very, very angry. "Who dares to come near my cave?" he yelled. Then he looked outside and saw Jack.

"I'll kill you," he called. "I'll eat you for my supper!"

He ran after Jack. But just before he reached him, he fell in the pit. Crash! Jack had his ax ready. While the giant was lying on the ground, Jack cut off his head.

Jack ran all the way home. He told his father. He told the farmers. They were so happy they gave Jack a sword. They They named him "Jack the Giant-killer."

Days passed. Everyone was happy. But then Jack heard about another monster. His name was Blunderbore! He lived in a castle in a beautiful forest.

Jack set out. But the day was hot. And he did not get very far before he lay down under a tree and fell asleep. Soon Blunderbore came along. He saw Jack, picked him up, and carried him to his castle.

Jack was put in a locked room. He was very afraid. Through the windows he could see the giant's other prisoners crying.

"This is awful," he said to himself. "I must find a way out."

Just then Jack heard voices below. He looked out his prison window. Blunderbore and another giant were going into the castle. "What to do? What to do?" he said. Then he saw a rope in the corner of his room. He made a noose and threw it over the two giants' heads. Then he held on to it with all his might. He pulled it tighter and tighter until both giants were dead.

Jack slid down the rope. He took the giants' keys from his pocket. He set free all the people who were locked in the castle. And he felt very good!

The next night he found himself at another castle. He knocked. To his sur-prise the door was opened by a giant with three heads. "Oh dear!" thought Jack. But the giant was very friendly. He even gave Jack a bed for the night.

Now, Jack learned that this giant had four treasures. A coat that made him invisible. A cap that told him all he wanted to know. A sword that could cut anything. And shoes that could carry him as fast as the wind. Jack wanted them all. So Jack went to bed, and thought how he could get them. But soon he fell asleep. Then he heard someone singing:

"Though you stay with me tonight,
  You shall not see the morning light;
  My club will kill you quite."

"Ho, ho!" cried Jack. He looked around for the wood he had seen by the fire-

place. Then he put the log in his bed and waited. Soon, the door opened. In came the giant! He walked up to the bed. Down came the club. Crash! Crash! Jack was very glad he wasn't in bed.

"Good-bye, my young friend," the giant said. "You'll make me a fine dinner by and by."

Jack had a good laugh over this. And when the giant had gone, he went back to bed.

In the morning Jack walked into the room where the giant was eating. "Good morning," he said. The giant was so surprised to see Jack that he didn't know what to say.

Jack sat down and ate a good break-fast. But all the time he was thinking. Suddenly he had a good idea. He waited until the giant was not looking. Then he hid as much of the pudding in his shirt as he could. As soon as breakfast was over, Jack said to the giant:

"I can plunge a knife into my shirt without hurting myself. I bet you can't!"

"I can do anything you can!" said the giant.

So Jack picked up a knife. He stuck it into his shirt. But all it cut was the pudding.

The giant pulled out his own knife. He

stuck it straight into his chest. Then he fell down dead.

Then Jack took the cap and the shoes and the coat and the sword, and went on his way. At the next castle a ball was taking place. The knights and ladies had all heard of Jack. They asked him to come in. He danced and had a very good time. But suddenly all the fun stopped. A big, angry giant was on his way to the castle.

"Have no fear," said Jack. He put on his invisible coat. "Leave everything to me."

He put on the shoes which carried him like the wind. Then he went out.

Now around the castle there was a moat. The giant was standing on the drawbridge that went across it. He roared in an awful voice:

"Fee, fi, fo, fum!
  I smell the blood of an Englishman;
  Be he alive, or be he dead,
  I'll grind his bones to make
      my bread!"

"You must catch me first!" cried Jack.

He took off his coat. Then he made the giant chase him around the castle.

Jack ran until he came again to the drawbridge. He ran across. When he got to the other side he cut the bridge in two with his magic sword—just as the giant was halfway across. Crash! Down went the giant. And that was the end of him.

Jack had many other adventures. And when he was tired of them all he went home again. He married a beautiful princess who he loved dearly.

FOLK TALES FROM OTHER LANDS

THE STUBBORN YOUNG MAN

Many, many years ago there was a powerful king. He ruled his country with an iron hand. Everybody was afraid of him. When he spoke the people shook. When he sneezed everyone had to say "To your good health." And they all did—except for one young man. He would not say "To your good health" when the king sneezed.

So this went on for quite a while. But one day the king found out about the young man. "Bring him to me at once!" he said.

The king sat on his throne. He looked down at the young man. Then he said, "Say it. Say to my good health!"

"To my good health!"

"To mine, to mine, you fool!"

"To mine, to mine, Your Majesty."

"But to mine. To my own," shouted the King. He got up and he looked very tall!

"Of course," said the young man. "To my own."

The king came close to the young man and roared: "Say 'To your health, Your Majesty' Or you will die!"

The young man shook his head. "Not until I marry your daughter."

Now the king's daughter was as pretty as a snow flower. She smiled at the young man. But the king did not smile at all. He had the young man thrown into a deep pit with a very hungry bear. And then everybody went away.

But there was something about the young man that touched the heart of the hungry bear. For the bear just sat back.

He looked at the young man the whole night through. He did not hurt him in any way. In the morning, the king came and found him alive.

"Well?" said the king.

"Not until I marry your daughter."

So this time the young man was thrown into a den of wild boars. Everyone was sure he was in for trouble. But he was not. In the morning the king found the young man. He was in the middle of the wild boars. They looked at him with love in their eyes.

"Well?" stormed the king. He was more angry than ever.

"Your daughter."

"Never!"

The king had once been given a present of two lions. They were his favorite pets. And they were mean and hungry! He had the young man thrown to the lions.

But the lions did not kill the young man. They spent the whole night licking his face!

Now the king had a new plan.

"Come with me," he said to the young man.

They rode along in the royal coach. Then they came to a forest. The trees were made of sparkling silver.

"This is all yours," the king said, "if you say 'To your good health, Your Majesty.' "

The young man looked at the silver forest. He would have given almost anything to own it.

Yet he said: "No."

The king and the young man rode on and on. They came to a very big castle of gold. When the sun shone upon it, it was dazzling.

"Say it and you shall have the forest and the castle."

The young man almost gave in. But then he said, "No."

They rode on and on until they came to a lake. On the lake were thousands of small boxes. In the boxes were jewels! The young man looked as if he wanted them more than anything in the world.

The king smiled. Now he was sure that he had won.

"Say it and you shall have it all—the forest, the castle, and all of these jewels."

Slowly the young man shook his head. "I love your daughter and I will marry her."

The king sat back in his coach. His face turned red. He hit the seats. He stamped his feet.

"All right!" He yelled, "All right! You may marry her. But will you say, 'To your good health, Your Majesty?' "

"Yes."

The wedding of the king's daughter and the young man was the best wedding ever seen. Such joy and such food and so many songs! Everybody was happy. The king was so happy that he began to sneeze. And everybody said what they had to say—"To your very good health, Your Majesty!" And then there was a great silence. All the faces were turned to the young man.

First, he gave his pretty bride a kiss. Then he turned to the king and said in a loud voice: "To your very good health, Your Majesty!"

And everybody cheered and cheered. For all I know, they are still cheering.

THE YOUNG MAN IN LOVE

There was once a young man. He was handsome. He worked hard. And he was poor. One bright, sunny day he was busy fixing the wall of a very rich man's home. As he worked he saw the man's beautiful daughter. Right then and there he said, "I must have this girl for my own."

"I want you for my wife," he said to the girl.

"You must ask my father," she said. All the time her eyes looked into his.

"I want your daughter for my wife," he said to the father.

"You do?" asked the father. He began to laugh.

"I will be a good husband to her and a good son-in-law to you."

The father laughed some more. Then shook his head.

"No you won't. Not until you bring me three treasures."

"What are they?"

"A strand of red hair three yards long. A golden rooster that has one foot. A pearl that glows like the sun even in the middle of the night."

"I will get them."

The rich man laughed and laughed. No one could find these things—because they weren't anywhere to be found!

But the young man was in love. So he want to try. He spent many days on strange roads. But he could not find even one of them. One night he was very tired. "I'll never find them," he said. "Never. It's no use." Then he had an idea. "I'll ask the Great Buddha for help." So he jumped up and began to walk to the Sacred Temple of the Great Buddha.

The very next night he stopped to rest at a house. An old woman lived there with her only son. The young man said he was on his way to the Temple. And the old woman asked for a favor.

"My son cannot speak. Please ask the Buddha what can be done to make him speak."

"I will ask him," said the young man. The very next evening he stopped at a farm. The farmer was very kind. Then he also asked a favor of him. "I just filled my storehouse with rice. But now there is nothing left. Please ask Buddha why."

"I will ask," said the young man and he went on his way.

He came to a river. There was no

bridge he could cross. There was no boat he could take. Suddenly a big snake arose from the river. He smiled at the young man.

"I will take you across if you ask the Buddha a question."

"What is it?"

"I have been in this river for five hundred years. Why have I not become a spirit?"

"Have you been a good snake?"

"Very good."

"Then I will ask the Buddha."

The young man came to the Sacred Temple of the Great Buddha. He was very tired. So he lay down and went to sleep. As he slept, he had a dream. Buddha came to him and said, "The old woman's son cannot speak because there is a red strand three yards long in his hair. A golden rooster with only one foot eats all the farmer's rice. A pearl that glows in the night is in the head of the snake. It keeps him from becoming a spirit."

In the morning the young man woke up. He was sure that his questions had been answered. He knelt and thanked the Buddha. Then went on his way.

He came to the broad river. The snake

was waiting for him. He took him across the river.

"Now I shall make you a spirit. I will pull out the pearl from your head," said the young man.

So he pulled out the pearl. Right then the snake became a spirit. He flew up into the blue sky. The young man looked at the pearl in his hand. It was glowing.

Next he came to the farm. He said to the farmer: "There is a golden rooster hiding in your storehouse. He eats all the rice."

The farmer found the golden rooster and gave him to the young man. And as he did so, the storehouse began to fill with rice.

Then the young man went to the old woman's house. "Let me cut the red strand that is three yards long from your son's hair," he said.

"Is that what the Buddha said to do?"
"Yes."
"Then do it."

He cut the long strand of red hair and the boy began to speak.

"Good-bye. Good luck to you," said his happy mother.

And, yes. The young man did have very good luck. He went to the rich father and showed him the three treasures. There was nothing the man could say but "Now you can have my daughter for your bride."

And there was nothing the daughter could say but "And now I shall be your bride."

And there was nothing for the happy young man to say but "I shall be a good husband to you. And a good son-in-law to you, dear father."

And he was.

HANSEL AND GRETEL

Near a great forest there lived a poor man, his wife, and their two children. The boy's name was Hansel. The girl's name was Gretel. The family was so poor! They often went to bed without any supper. One night the man said to his wife:

"What will become of us? We cannot even feed our children."

"I will tell you what," said the wife. "We will take the children into the forest early in the morning. We will make them a fire, and give each of them a piece of bread. Then we will go to our work and leave them alone. They will never find the way home again. We shall be rid of them."

"No, wife," said the man, "I cannot do that. I cannot take my children into the forest and leave them. The wild animals would eat them."

"O you fool," said she. All four of us will starve. Do you want us all to die?" And she would not leave him alone. She kept talking about taking the children into the woods.

"But I feel sorry for them!" said the man.

The two hungry children had not been able to sleep. So they heard what their stepmother had said. Gretel said to Hansel, "What are we going to do?"

"Do be quiet, Gretel," said Hansel, "and do not worry. I will think of something." And when the parents were asleep, he got up and went out. The moon was shining. The white stones in front of the house looked like pieces of silver. Hansel filled the little pocket of his coat. Then he went back again, and said to Gretel.

"Do not worry, dear little sister. Go to sleep quietly. We will be all right." He went back to his bed again.

The next day the stepmother woke the two children up.

"Get up, you lazybones," she said. "We are going into the forest to cut wood."

Then she gave each of them a piece of bread, and said:

"That is for dinner. Don't eat it before then. You will get no more."

Gretel carried the bread under her apron, because Hansel's pocket was full of stones. Then they all set off for the forest. When they had gone a little way, Hansel stood still. He looked back at the house. He did this so often his father said:

"Hansel, what are you looking at?"

"O father," said Hansel, "I am looking at my little white kitten. She is sitting up on the roof saying good-bye."

"You fool," said the woman, "that is not your kitten. It is the sun shining on the chimney."

Of course, Hansel had not been looking at his kitten at all. But every now and then he dropped a stone from his pocket on the road.

When they reached the middle of the forest, the father told the children to get some wood. "Now, make a fire and keep warm," he said. Hansel and Gretel found enough wood for a little fire. When the flames were leaping quite high the wife said:

"Now lie down by the fire and rest. We will cut the wood. When we are ready we will come and get you."

So Hansel and Gretel sat by the fire. At noon they ate their bread. They thought their father was in the wood all the time. They seemed to hear the stroke of the axe. But really it was only a

dry branch moving back and forth in the wind. They stayed there a long time. Soon they were very tired. They fell fast asleep. It was night when they woke up. Gretel said:

"How shall we ever get out of this wood?"

But Hansel said:

"Wait a little while longer. When the moon comes up, we can find the way home."

The full moon rose. Hansel took his little sister by the hand. They followed the stones shining like silver. They walked on the whole night. At the break of day they came to their father's house. They knocked at the door. When the wife saw Hansel and Gretel, she said:

"You bad children, why did you sleep so long in the wood? We thought you were never coming home again!"

But the father was glad. He had been awake all night worrying about them.

Not very long after that the family was very poor again. One night the children heard their mother say:

"Everything has been eaten. We have only half a loaf of bread. After that is gone, the children must go. We will take them further into the wood this time. They will not be able to find the way back again. There is nothing else we can do."

The man felt sad and he thought, "It would be better to share your last bit of food with your children."

But the wife would not listen. She talked and talked until the man gave in.

The children were not asleep. They had heard all that was said. When the parents had gone to sleep, Hansel got up to get some stones. But the wife had locked the door. Hansel could not get out. He said to his little sister:

"Do not cry, Gretel. Go to sleep. I will think of something."

Early the next morning the step-mother came and pulled the children out of bed. She gave them each a little piece of bread. It was even smaller than before. On the way to the wood Hansel broke up the bread. He often stopped to throw a crumb on the ground.

"Hansel, why do you keep looking behind you?" asked his father.

"I am looking at my little pigeon. She is sitting on the roof to say good-bye to me," said Hansel.

"You fool," said the wife, "that is no pigeon. It is the sun shining on the chimney."

Hansel went on as before. He threw bread crumbs all along the road.

The woman led the children far into the wood. They had never been this far before. Again they made a fire. The wife said:

"Now you sit still here, children. When you are tired you can go to sleep. We are going into the forest to cut wood. In the evening, when we are ready to go home, we will come and get you."

So when noon came Gretel gave some of her bread to Hansel. Then they went to sleep. The evening passed. No one came for the poor children. When they awoke it was dark. Hansel said:

"Wait a little, Gretel, until the moon comes up. Then we shall be able to see our way home. The crumbs of bread will show us which way to go."

So when the moon was bright, they got up. But they could find no crumbs of bread. The birds had eaten them all! Hansel thought they might find the way all the same. But they could not. They walked all that night, and all the next day. But they could not find the way out of the wood. They were very hungry. They had nothing to eat except the few berries they could find. When they were so tired that they could not walk anymore, they lay down under a tree and fell asleep.

It was now the third morning since they had left their father's house. All that time they had been trying to find their way home. But they were only going deeper into the wood. About noon they saw a pretty bird sitting in a tree. It sang so well they stopped to listen. Then the bird spread his wings and flew before them. They followed him until they came to a little house. The bird sat on the roof. When they came nearer they saw that the house was built of bread.

The roof was made of cakes! The windows were sugar!

"We will have some of this," said Hansel. "It will make a fine meal! I will eat a piece of the roof. You can have some of the window. That will taste sweet."

So Hansel broke off a bit of the roof. Gretel stood by the window and ate a piece. Then they heard a thin voice call out:

"Nibble, nibble, like a mouse,
Who is nibbling at my house?"

And the children said:

"Never mind.
It is the wind."

So they went on eating. They didn't think about the voice.

Hansel thought the roof tasted very nice. So he took down a great piece of it. Gretel pulled out a large round window-pane. She sat down and began to eat it. Then the door opened. An old woman came out. Hansel and Gretel were very afraid. They dropped what they were eating. But the old woman said:

"Ah, my dear children, how did you get here? You must come inside and stay with me. You will be no trouble."

She then led them into her little house. They had a good meal of milk and pancakes, with sugar, apples, and nuts. After they had eaten, she showed them two little white beds. Hansel and Gretel lay down on them. They thought they were in heaven.

Now the old woman seemed very kind. But she was really a wicked witch. She had built this little house just to catch children. Once they were inside she killed them, cooked them, and ate them. The witch's eyes were red. She could not see very far. But she had a good nose. She could smell when children were nearby. When she knew Hansel and Gretel were coming, she gave a laugh, and said:

"I have them! They shall not get away."

Early in the morning, before the children were awake, she got up to look at them. There they were! They looked so nice with their red cheeks. The old witch said to herself:

"What a fine dinner I shall have!"

Then she grabbed Hansel. She led them into a little barn where she shut him up. He called and screamed. But she would not let him go. Then she went back to Gretel and shook her.

"Get up, lazybones," she said. "Go get some water. Cook something nice for your brother. He is out in the barn. Feed him and when he is fat enough I will eat him."

Gretel began to cry. But it was no use. She had to do what the witch told her.

And so the best kind of food was cooked for poor Hansel. Gretel got nothing. Each morning the old woman went to the barn and said:

"Hansel, give me your finger. I want to know if you are fat enough."

But Hansel gave her a little bone. And the old woman could not see what it was. She thought it was Hansel's finger. "Why aren't you getting fat, you silly child?" she said. And she went back to the house. After four weeks had passed Hansel seemed to be as thin as ever. The witch could not wait anymore.

"Now then, Gretel," she said, "be quick. Get some water. I don't care if Hansel is fat or thin. Tomorrow I must kill and cook him."

Oh how awful for the poor little girl to have to get the water! How she cried for her brother!

"Dear God, help us!" she said. "If we had been eaten by wild animals in the wood, at least we should have died together."

"Stop crying," said the old woman, "it will do you no good."

Early next morning Gretel had to make the fire and fill the kettle.

"First we will do the baking," said the old woman. "I have heated the oven. The dough is ready."

She pushed poor Gretel toward the oven. The flames were leaping out.

"Creep in," said the witch. See if it is hot enough to bake the bread."

Once Gretel was in, the witch was going to shut the door on her. Then she would cook her and eat her. But Gretel saw what she meant to do, and said:

"I don't know how to do it. How shall I get in?"

"Stupid goose," said the old woman. "Can't you see that the opening is big enough? I could get in myself!" She bent down and put her head in the oven. Then Gretel gave her such a push. She fell in. Gretel shut the iron door. Oh, how the wicked witch howled! But Gretel ran away, and left her to burn. Gretel quickly opened the barn door and cried:

"Hansel, we are free! The old witch is dead."

Then out flew Hansel like a bird from its cage. How happy they both were!

They danced about and kissed each other. Then they looked all over the old witch's house. In every corner there were chests of pearls and gold.

"These are better than stones!" said Hansel. He filled his pocket. Gretel filled her apron full.

"Now, away we go," said Hansel. "If we can only get out of the witch's wood."

After they had been walking for a few hours they saw a big pond.

"We can never get across this," said Hansel. "I see no stepping-stones. There is no bridge."

"And there is no boat either," said Gretel. "But here comes a white duck. If I ask her she will help us over." So she cried:

"Duck, duck, here we stand,
Hansel and Gretel, on the land,
Stepping-stones and bridge we lack,
Carry us over on your nice white
    back."

And the duck came and carried them across. After that they came to their own wood. And then they knew the way. At last they saw their father's house. They ran until they reached it. They went in and fell on their father's neck. The man had not had a quiet sleep since he left his children in the wood.

His wife had been very angry because he could only think of his children. So she went away. And Hansel and Gretel and their father lived happily ever after.

THE TINDER BOX

A soldier came marching along the road—one, two! one, two! He had a sack on his back. He had a sword by his side. He had been in the wars. Now he wanted to go home. And on the way he met an old witch. She was very ugly.

"Good evening, soldier," she said. "What a fine sword you have. What a big sack! Now you will have as much money as you want."

"I thank you, old witch," said the soldier.

"Do you see that tree?" asked the witch. "It is empty inside. You must climb to the top. Then you'll see a hole. You can let yourself down into the tree. I'll tie a rope around you. Then I can pull you up when you call."

"What am I to do when I'm in the tree?" asked the soldier.

"Get the money," said the witch. "Listen to me. Get down to the earth under the tree. You will find a great room. It is quite light. Many lamps are burning there. Then you will see three doors. These you can open. The keys are in the locks. If you go into the first room, you will see a big chest. On it sits a dog. He has eyes as big as teacups. But do not worry. I'll give you my apron. You can put it on the floor. Then go quickly and take the dog. Set him on my apron. Open the chest. Take as many coins as you like. They are copper. If you want silver, you must go into the second room.

"Here sits a dog with eyes as big as plates. But do not worry. Put him on my apron and take some money. If you want gold, you can have that too. Go into the third room. The dog that sits in the chest in that room has eyes as big as wheels. He is a fierce dog, you may be sure. But do not be afraid. Put him on my apron. Then he will not hurt you. Take as much gold as you like."

"That's not so bad," said the soldier. "But what do you want, you old witch? You are not doing this for nothing."

"I only want an old tinder box," said the witch. "It was my grandmother's and I would like to have it."

So the soldier climbed into the tree. He let himself down the hole. And just as the witch had said, he was in a great room.

Then he opened the first door. Ugh! There was the dog with eyes as big as teacups. "You're a nice dog," said the soldier. He set the dog on the witch's apron. Then he took as many copper coins as his pockets would hold. He locked the chest, put the dog back, and went into the second room. Aha! There was the dog with eyes as big as plates.

"You should not stare at me," said the soldier. "You might hurt your eyes." He put the dog on the witch's apron. When he saw the silver money, he threw away all the copper coins. Then he filled his pockets and his sack with silver. At last he went into the third room. Oh, but that was horrid! The dog had eyes as big as wheels. They turned round and round in his head!

"Good evening!" said the soldier and he took off his hat. He had never seen a dog like this before! Slowly he put him on the apron. Then he opened the chest. My! There was so much gold! He could buy anything he wanted with it! He threw away the silver coins and took the gold. Then he put the dog on the chest and shut the door. He called up through the tree, "Now pull me up, you old witch."

"Have you got the tinder box?" asked the witch.

"Bones and stones!" said the soldier. "I forgot it." So he went and found it.

The witch pulled him up. He stood on the road again. His pockets, boots, sack, and hat were filled with gold.

"What are you going to do with the tinder box?" the soldier asked.

"That doesn't have anything to do with you," said the witch. "You have your money. Just give me the tinder box!"

"Tell me," said the soldier, "or I'll cut off your head."

"No!" said the witch.

So the soldier cut off her head. There she lay! He tied up all his money in her apron and put it on his back like a sack. Then he put the tinder box in his pocket and went to town.

It was a fine town! He went to the best inn. He asked for the most beautiful rooms. He ate his favorite food. He was rich! The servant who cleaned his boots thought they were very old for such a rich man. But the soldier had not had time to buy new ones yet. So the next day he did. He got new boots and fine clothes. Now he looked like a real gentleman.

The next day he took a walk around the town. The people told him of all the great things there were to see and do. They told him about the king and his very pretty daughter.

"How can I see her?" asked the soldier.

"Oh, you can't!" said the people. "She lives in a castle. There are many walls and towers around it. No one but the king can go in there."

"Why is that?" asked the soldier.

The people said, "When the princess was born, it was foretold that she would marry a soldier. The king does not want that to happen. So no one may see her."

"I would like to see her," said the soldier. But he could not think of a way to do it.

So the soldier lived very well. He went to plays. He drove in the king's garden. He gave a lot of money to the poor. This was very kind of him. He remembered how hard life was when he did not have any money. Now he was rich. So he gave to the poor. He also had many friends. They all said he was a fine man. That pleased the soldier. But every day he spent money. He never earned any. Soon he had only a few coins left.

He had to move out of his fine rooms. So he went to live in a little place. He had to clean his own boots. He fixed his own clothes. None of his friends came to see him anymore. There were too many steps to climb to get to his room.

One night it was very dark. And he could not even buy a candle. He didn't have enough money. Then he remembered. There was a candle in the tinder box! He got the tinder box and the candle. But as soon as he struck a fire, the door flew open. The dog with the eyes as big as teacups stood before him.

"What do you want, my lord?" said the dog.

"What is this?" said the soldier. He clapped his hands. "I know. It is the tinder box. Now I can have everything I

want! Bring me some money," he said to the dog. And whisk! The dog was gone. Whisk! He was back again. He had a bag full of money in his mouth.

Now the soldier knew how great the tinder box was. If he struck it once, he called the dog who sat on the copper coins. If he struck it twice, the dog who had the silver came. If he struck it three times, he called the dog who had the gold. Now the soldier moved back to his fine rooms. All his friends knew him again. And they cared very much for him.

One day he said to himself, "It is very strange that I cannot get to see the princess. They all say she is very beautiful. But what good is that? She always has to sit in her castle. Can I not see her at all? Where is my tinder box? He struck a light and whisk! There was the dog with eyes as big as teacups.

"It is very late," said the soldier, "but I would like to see the princess."

The dog went outside. And whisk! Before the soldier could speak again, he came back with the princess. She sat on his back, sleeping.

The soldier could see she was a real princess. She was so beautiful! He could not stop himself from kissing her. Then the dog ran back to the castle.

When morning came, the king and queen were drinking tea. The princess told them she had a strange dream. It was about a dog and a soldier. She said she had ridden on a dog and kissed a soldier.

"That's a fine story!" said the queen. But that night she had one of her ladies sit by the princess's bed. She wanted to see if the story really was a dream.

Now the soldier wanted to see the beautiful princess again. So the dog came in the night. He took her away as fast as he could. But the old lady who was watching put on her boots. She ran just as fast as the dog. So she saw that they both went into a fine house. "Now I know what is going on!" said the old

lady. She took some chalk and put a big cross on the door of the house.

When the dog took the princess back, he saw the cross on the door. So he took some chalk and drew a cross on every door. Now the lady would not be able to find the right one!

The next day, the lady showed the king and queen where the princess had been. "Here it is!" said the king.

"No, my dear, it is here!" said the queen.

"There it is! There it is!" they all said. Wherever they looked, there was a cross on the door. So they saw that it would do no good to keep on looking.

But the queen was very smart. She took her great gold scissors. She cut up a piece of cloth. Then she made a nice little bag. She put flour in the bag and tied it to the princess. When that was done, she cut a small hole in the bag. Now the flour would fall on the ground—a little bit at a time. And she would know where the princess was being taken!

That night the dog came back again. He took the princess. Then he ran with her to the soldier who loved her very much. The solder really wanted her for his wife.

As the dog ran, he did not see the flour. It made a path from the castle to the soldier's house. But in the morning the king and queen saw it! Now they knew where their daughter had been. They took the soldier and put him in prison.

There he sat. Oh, it was so dark and awful! The guards said to him, "Tomorrow you shall be hanged." This was not fun to hear! And he had left his tinder box at the inn.

The next day, he looked through the iron bars on his window. How the people were hurrying to see him hanged! He heard the drums beat. He saw the soldiers march. All the people were running about. Among them was a young boy. He was running so fast that one of his shoes flew off. It hit the wall where the soldier was looking through the bars.

"Hello, boy! You don't have to run," the soldier said. "The hanging will not begin until I come. But first I need you to do something. Run to where I live. Bring my tinder box. Then you shall have four coins. But you must go as fast as you can."

The boy wanted to get the four coins. So he got the tinder box.

The gallows had been built outside of town. Around it, there were many important people. The king and queen sat on their thrones. Everyone was ready—even the soldier. But as they put the rope around his neck, he said, "Stop! Don't you know? Before a man is hanged, he is always given one last favor. So I would like to smoke a pipe of tobacco."

The king could not say "no" to this. So the soldier took out his tinder box and struck fire. One—two—three! Suddenly there were all the dogs. The one with eyes as big as teacups. The one with eyes as large as plates. The one with eyes like wheels that went around and around.

"Help me now!" said the soldier. "I do not want to hang!"

"No!" cried the king. But the largest dog took him and the queen and threw them into the air. Now everyone was afraid. The people said, "Soldier, you shall be our King. Marry the beautiful princess."

So they put the soldier into the king's coach. The three dogs danced in front. Everyone clapped and sang. Little boys whistled through their fingers. The princess came out of the castle. The wedding lasted a week. And the three dogs sat at the wedding table too. They opened their eyes wider than ever at all the things they saw.

RIP VAN WINKLE

Long ago there lived a man named Rip Van Winkle. His father had left him a farm. Around the farm were some of the finest mountains in the world. But Rip Van Winkle was not happy. His wife always yelled at him. And to tell the truth, you might have yelled at him too.

Rip Van Winkle never did more than two days work in a week. He was always ready to make kites. He loved to tell stories to his children. He loved to hunt and fish. But he did not love to work on the farm. So his family was poor and his wife yelled more every day.

One day, Rip Van Winkle's wife was yelling even more than usual. So he left the house and went to the village. But his wife followed him. So he took his dog and his gun and went up into the mountains. The beautiful, strange mountains—where many people were afraid to go.

It was late in the day when he stopped to rest on a hill. Now Rip Van Winkle—as you know—did nothing very well. So he lay there doing nothing until it began to get dark. He was just getting hungry when he heard a voice calling, "Rip Van Winkle! Rip Van Winkle!" He looked around but all he saw was a bird flying across the mountain. Then he heard the voice again, "Rip Van Winkle! Rip Van Winkle." This time his dog stood up and growled. A long, deep growl.

Rip looked down and what do you think he saw! A strange little man was walking toward him. "Who are you?" asked Rip. But the little man did not answer.

As Rip went toward the little man, his dog began to bark—as if to say, Don't go! But Rip did not listen. He walked up to the little man. This is what he saw.

The little man was very fat. And he had on very strange clothes! Rip had never seen anything like them before. On his back, he had a big, heavy barrel. He made a sign for Rip to help him with the barrel. So Rip took one end and followed the man down a narrow path. There were big trees on both sides. Rip could not really see where he was going. They walked and walked—tripping over rocks. Low branches hit Rip in the face

and he began to feel very sorry that he had helped the little man.

Soon the forest opened into a clearing. In the middle was a funny-looking group of little men. They were bowling and laughing. Some of them were dressed like the fat little man.

When they saw Rip, they stopped their play and stared at him. Rip's knees knocked together. Now the little men opened the barrel. They made signs for Rip to drink with them. Rip was afraid. So he did what they wanted. They drank in silence. Then they returned to their game.

By-and-by Rip became less afraid. When no one was looking, he had a little more to drink. Whatever it was, it tasted very good! Soon he had another and another—until his eyes rolled in his head and he fell down. Then in no time at all, he was asleep.

When he awoke, the birds were singing. The sun was shining. He was lying on the hill where he and his dog had been.

"Oh, that wicked drink!" he said. "What shall I say to my wife? Oh, how stiff I feel! My gun is so rusty!"

He called to his dog. But he did not come. So he set off for home. On the way he met some strangers. They looked odd and they stared at him. But he walked on until he came on his own house. But there was no more house! Just a heap of ruins. Rip stared in horror. He shouted for his wife. He shouted for his children. But no one answered.

He now ran to the village. A lot of people had heard about an odd man in their village. So they came to look at him. One of the men wanted to know who he was. When Rip told his story, no one believed him.

"Find my friends and neighbors," he said. "They know me. They know I tell the truth!"

He was told all his neighbors were dead. But soon a woman with a baby on her arm pushed through the crowd, and looked at him.

"My father was Rip Van Winkle," she said. "He went off to the mountains twenty years ago. His dog returned, but he never did. I think—yes, even with your gray beard and wrinkles—I think you are he!"

Rip Van Winkle suddenly saw that his years of youth and strength were gone. Everything had changed. His wife was dead. His friends were dead. He was a poor, useless old man. He covered his face with his hands.

But although he had not fed his children very well, his daughter was ready to feed him. She had married a farmer, and Rip Van Winkle made his home with them. Very soon he was, as he had been years before, the best story-teller to be found in the village.

BIBLE STORIES

NOAH'S ARK

The story of Noah is in the first book in the Bible. It tells how God looked at the world and saw that people had become wicked. So He said He would cover the earth with water and start again. He asked Noah, who was a good man, to help Him.

God told Noah to build a very large boat. It must be big enough to hold Noah and his family and two of every kind of animal that lived. It must be strong enough to stand against the great waters.

After God spoke to Noah, Noah began to build the boat. He called it an ark. His family helped him. They worked for many days without stopping.

Everyone laughed at Noah when they saw him working in the hot sun. They thought he was very silly to build a boat on dry land. But Noah did not listen. He just went on working.

At last the ark was ready. Now Noah had to get a male and a female of every kind of animal to go into the ark. When he had done this, he and his family went in too.

Then God sent the rain. It rained and rained without stopping. Soon the ark was floating on the water. And still the rain came—for forty days and forty nights. But Noah and his family and the animals were safe inside the ark.

Then the rain stopped. The sky was clear. The sun came out again. But the whole world was covered with water.

For 150 days the ark floated on the water. Then slowly the water began to go down. And one day Noah felt the boat bump against something. It had come to rest on a mountain called Mount Ararat.

Noah looked out to see if he could find any land. He saw nothing. So he took out a dove. He let it go. Then he watched it fly away. He knew that if it did not come back, it had found a place to land. But soon the dove returned.

Seven days passed. Noah sent the dove out again. It came back again—but this time it had a leaf in its beak. Now Noah knew the waters must have gone down enough for some of the trees to show.

He waited another seven days. Again he sent the dove out. It did not come back. Noah knew it had found a place to land and build a nest.

Soon the land around the ark was dry. God told Noah to send the animals on to the earth. Then Noah and his family left the ark. God also told Noah that He would never send a great flood again. He gave Noah a sign. It was a rainbow. Now when we see a rainbow we can remember God's promise to Noah and to all the people that came after him.

DANIEL IN THE LION'S DEN

Darius was a king. He had 120 princes watching out for his kingdom. Over these princes, he placed three men. The first and best was Daniel. Daniel was almost as important as the king himself.

The other princes did not like this. They began to think of a way to make the king angry with Daniel. At first they could not. Daniel was a good man who did everything right. But at last, they found a plan. They would ask the king to pass a law that Daniel could not obey. Then when Daniel broke the law, the king would have to punish him.

The next day the princes went to the king. They told him it was not good for the people in his kingdom to have different religions. They said, "It will be better if everyone does what you do." So the king listened. Then he passed a law that no one could pray to any god for the next thirty days. But still the princes were not happy. They made the king say that the law would never be changed.

Now the princes sat back to see what Daniel would do when he knew about the law. And Daniel did as he always had done. Every day he got on his knees and prayed to his God.

When the princes saw this they went to the king. "We have seen Daniel praying," they said. "He broke the law." The king was very sad. Now Daniel must be put into a den of lions. He tried to think of a way to save him. But there was none. The princes said, "You must punish him the way you would anyone else." So Daniel was put into the lion's den. The door was locked. He was left to die.

When the king heard, he could not eat. That night he could not sleep. He kept thinking about Daniel. In the morning, he went to the den. Sadly and without hope, he called out, "Has your God been able to save you from the lions?"

Daniel answered. The king was filled with joy. "God sent an angel," Daniel said. "He shut the lions' mouths."

Then the king said that Daniel should be free. The doors were opened. Daniel stood before him. He was not hurt.

Then princes were put into the den. No angel came to save them.

DAVID AND GOLIATH

Long ago a young boy named David lived in the land of Israel. It was a time of war. The Philistines were fighting with the Israelites. The two armies faced each other on top of a big mountain. There was a valley between them.

Now the Philistines had a great fighter. His name was Goliath. He was a giant of a man. Other men were afraid of him.

Goliath went down into the valley. He called out, "Choose one man to come and fight with me. If he kills me, we will be your servants. If I kill him, you will be our servants. Give me a man to fight!"

When Saul, the King of Israel, heard this he was upset and very much afraid.

Now David, the young boy, had three older brothers. They had all gone to war. But David had stayed with his father to care for the sheep. One day David's father said, "Go to the mountain. Take your brothers this food."

So David took the food to his brothers. As he talked to them, Goliath came into

the valley. Again he shouted to Israel to send a man to fight. David said, "Don't be afraid. I will fight Goliath."

But Saul told David he was only a boy. Goliath was a great fighter. The David said, "I keep my father's sheep. When a lion came and took a lamb, I killed him. I have also killed a bear. I shall kill Goliath because he is against the armies of God."

Saul said, "Go then. The Lord be with you." Then he asked David to wear his armor. But David said no. He did not need it. He took five stones from a brook. He took his slingshot and went down to meet Goliath.

Goliath saw David. He said, "Am I a dog? You have sent a boy to catch me! I will feed his body to the birds!"

David said, "You come with a spear. But I come in the name of the Lord."

Then David put a stone into his sling. He threw the stone at Goliath. It hit him in the forehead. The giant fell dead.

So David killed the great Goliath with one small stone. And he saved the land of Israel.

PUSS IN BOOTS

Once there was a miller. He had three sons. When he died, he left them everything he had. The oldest got the mill. The second son got the donkey. The youngest son got only what was left—a cat.

This worried the youngest son. He did not know how he would make a living. "My brothers can get together," he said. "They can use the donkey to work at the mill. But what can I do with a cat?"

The cat heard this. He sat up before his new master.

"Meow," he said. "Do not worry, my young friend. All you have to do is give me a sack. Make me a pair of boots so that I may run through the woods. Then you shall see. You are not as bad off as you think."

The young man smiled. But he knew this was no ordinary cat. He had seen him play many tricks to catch mice and rats. So he found an old sack. He set to work making two little boots. When they were done, the cat put on the boots. He hung the sack around his neck—holding the string in his paws.

"You will never be sorry you gave me these," said the cat. Then he was out of the door before the young man could blink.

First the cat went to a field. There were many rabbits. He put corn and carrots into his sack. Then he hid behind a rock. In a little while, a silly young rabbit came along. He ran into the sack to get the corn and carrots. Out jumped Puss. He pulled the strings. Then he took the sack to the palace. He asked to speak to the king.

"Your Majesty," he said. "I have a rabbit for you. It is from my lord, the Master of Carabas." (This was the name Puss made up for his master.)

The next day, the cat hid in a bush. He held his sack open. Then he made some sounds like a bird. Soon two fat birds came by. They heard the sounds and ran right into the open sack. Puss pulled the strings and went to see the king.

"These fat birds are from my lord, the Master of Carabas," he said.

This time the king gave Puss some money. He filled the sack with gold coins. Puss went back to his master. He was very pleased with himself.

His master was very surprised. He asked the cat how he got so much money. But the cat would not tell him.

On the third day, the cat caught two fine fish. He took them to the king.

"These are from my lord, the Master of Carabas," he said. And again the king gave him some money.

Now while the cat was walking home, he passed an inn. Two of the king's men

were sitting at a table talking. Puss thought he might learn something. So he stopped to listen.

The first man said, "The king has asked for his coach today. He wants to take a drive along the river."

The second man said, "Yes, and his beautiful daughter is going with him."

When Puss heard this he ran as fast as he could to find his master. "Come with me," he said. "Your fortune is made! You must swim in the river. I will show you where. Leave the rest to me."

The young man really didn't believe the cat. But he did what he asked to please him. Besides the water was warm. So he swam about having fun. And while he was in the water, Puss hid his old clothes under a rock. Then he ran out to the road to wait for the king.

When he saw the coach, he yelled, "Help! Help! My lord, the Master of Carabas, is drowning!"

The king told his driver to stop. Puss ran up. He pretended to be very afraid. "My master was swimming," he said. "And some thieves took his fine clothes! Now he will not come out of the river because he doesn't have anything to put on. I'm afraid he will drown."

coach. Soon he saw some workers in a field.

"Good people," said Puss. "The king is coming by. Tell him this field belongs to the Master of Carabas—or else you will be chopped into bits."

Then the cat ran away as fast as he could. He did not want the king to see him there.

A few minutes later, the king passed by. "Who owns this fine field?" he asked.

The people said, "My lord, the Master of Carabas." The king nodded and smiled.

Still Puss ran ahead. He saw some more farmers. "Good people," he said. "The king is coming by. You must tell him all this corn belongs to the Master of Carabas—or else you will be chopped into bits!"

When the king passed, he asked who owned the corn.

The people said, "My lord, the Master of Carabas." When the king heard this, he was well pleased. He told the young man how fine his corn was.

Now the young man began to see what Puss was up to. But he dared not say anything. So he sat there and looked at the princess. The most beautiful princess in the whole world looked back at him.

At last Puss came to a forest. In the middle was a castle. It belonged to a wicked ogre. In fact, all the lands the king was riding through belonged to this ogre. For years the farmers had to work for this cruel master.

"What do you want?" the ogre roared. He opened the door and saw the cat.

"Nothing," said the cat. "I have heard how wonderful you are. I wanted to see for myself. Is it true what they say? Can you really change yourself into a lion?"

"It is true," said the ogre. He rolled his eyes and showed his big teeth.

The king was very upset. He remembered the rabbit, the two birds, and the fish. So he told one of his men to get some clothes for the Master of Carabas. Then he sent his guards to help him out of the river.

When the fine clothes came, the young man was too surprised to speak. He just put them on. And he looked so fine that the king asked him to ride in the coach. So the young man sat across from the king and his beautiful daughter. She looked at him for a long time. Never had she seen such a handsome man. Right there, she fell in love with him.

The cat was very happy. His plan was working! He ran along in front of the

"I don't believe it," said the cat. There was a clap of thunder. And a lion was standing in front of the cat.

"Now do you believe it?" roared the lion.

"Oh, well," said the cat, "it's easy to make yourself larger. But I don't believe you can make yourself small—as small as a mouse."

There was another clap of thunder. The lion was gone. Instead there was a tiny mouse. Puss jumped on the mouse and ate him up.

Just then the king drove up. When he saw the castle, he wanted to go inside.

Puss heard the coach. He ran outside and said, "Welcome! Welcome to the home of my lord, the Master of Carabas!"

"What!" said the king. "This fine castle belongs to you? Let's go inside."

Inside a wonderful dinner was waiting. The ogre had just made it for himself. The king was so happy with the food and the castle and the handsome young man. He asked the young man to marry his daughter.

So the young man and the princess were married. Puss danced at the wedding in his shiny little boots.

THE GINGERBREAD MAN

Once a little boy lived far off in the country where there were no other boys and girls. He was often very sad.

One day his mother said, "I will bake a Gingerbread Man. You can play with him."

So she took some flour and molasses and cream and sugar and eggs and ginger and baking powder. She mixed them all together and cut out a Gingerbread Man. Next she made round black eyes out of raisins. She gave him a funny nose and a happy mouth. She put little red candies down his jacket for buttons. Then she put him in the oven. "Watch him to make sure he does not burn," she said.

The little boy sat in front of the oven door. He watched and watched and watched. First he saw the Gingerbread Man begin to grow. Then it got brown. Then he saw . . . what do you think he saw! His mother had put in *too much baking powder*! Now the Gingerbread Man began to rise . . . and rise . . . and rise . . . right out of the pan . . . and out of the oven! Before the boy could catch him, the Gingerbread Man ran out of the house. He ran down the road. He ran as fast as his brown legs would go.

"Stop!" yelled the mother. "Stop!" yelled the little boy. "We made you! You are ours!" But the Gingerbread Man did not stop. He laughed and said,

"Run, run, as fast as you can.
I got out of the oven and out
 of the pan.
And you'll never catch this
 Gingerbread Man."

And the mother and her son could not catch him. The Gingerbread Man ran on and on. Then he met a cow.

"Stop, Mr. Gingerbread Man!" said the cow. "Don't run so fast. Stay and let me eat you up." But the Gingerbread Man just laughed and said,

"Run, run, as fast as you can,
I got out of the oven and out
 of the pan.
And you'll never catch this
 Gingerbread Man."

The cow ran after him as fast as she could. But she could not catch him. Next the Gingerbread Man met a horse in a field.

"Stop, Mr. Gingerbread Man!" said the horse. "Do not run so fast. Stay and let me eat you up." But the Gingerbread Man ran faster than ever. He jumped over a fence and said,

"Run, run as fast as you can!
Everyone's after the Gingerbread
 Man.
The boy, the mother, the old red cow,
So you can try to catch me now!"

The horse ran after him as fast as he could. But he could not catch him. The Gingerbread Man just ran on and on. Then he came to a field. Some farmers were picking corn.

"Stop, Mr. Gingerbread Man," said the farmers. "Stay and rest a while."

"No, thank you," said the Gingerbread Man. "I cannot rest here. You will eat me up!" he ran past them and laughed.

"Run, run, as fast as you can.
Everyone's after the Gingerbread
  Man.
The boy and the mother, the horse
  and the cow,
So you can try to catch me now."

And all the farmers left their work.
They ran and ran. But they did not catch
him.

By now the sun had baked the Gingerbread Man. And he made the air smell
sweet and good. As he ran along some
woodcutters smelled him. They dropped
their axes and came running.

"Stop, Mr. Gingerbread Man," they
said. "You smell so good. Let us eat you
up."

But the Gingerbread Man ran out of
the woods as fast as he could. He
laughed and said,

"Run, run, as fast as you can.
Everyone's after the Gingerbread
  Man!
The boy and the mother, the horse
  and the cow,
And the farmers. So you can try
  to catch me now."

But the woodcutters could not catch
him. So the Gingerbread Man felt very
good. He began to dance and sing. No
one would ever catch him now!

And no one ever did. But someone did
eat him up. It was someone who never
ran after him at all! Here's how it happened. As the Gingerbread Man danced
along—thinking he was so smart—a
drop of rain fell on him. He looked up at
the sky. He saw the dark clouds and he
was afraid. Rain would make his legs
soft! Someone would catch him!

Just then a pig came out of the woods.
"Good day," said the pig.

"Good day to you," said the Gingerbread Man. He began to run away.

"Don't go," said the pig. "I cannot chase
you. I am too fat. But I can help you get
away from the rain."

"Oh?" said the Gingerbread Man.
"How can you do that?"

"Sit on my back," said the pig. "Then
your feet will not get wet. We can go and
hide from the rain."

"That is a good idea," said the Gingerbread Man. So he got on the pig's back.
But the pig's back was too round.

"Sit on my nose," said the pig. "Then
you will not fall off."

"That is a good idea," said the Gingerbread Man.

So the silly Gingerbread Man sat on
the pig's nose and—"Oink! Oink!" The
pig turned his nose and down fell the
Gingerbread Man. Right into the pig's
mouth! And the pig ate him all up.

So that was the end of the Gingerbread Man and the end of the story.

FABLES FROM LONG AGO

A fable is a story made up to teach a lesson. Most of them are very old—but the lessons are just as good now as they were then. Here are a few old favorites.

THE GOOSE THAT WAS JUST A GOOSE

Once a goose was very proud of her white feathers. So she tried to pretend she was a swan. She left her family and swam around the pond. She bent her neck like a swan's.

But it was no use. Her neck was too short and stiff. Nobody thought she was a swan. She just looked silly.

It is no use trying to make people think we are something that we aren't.

THE DOG IN THE HAY

One day a dog jumped into some hay. Then he went to sleep. In a little while, an ox came by. The ox wanted to eat the hay.

When the dog heard the ox, he got up and barked. The ox was ready to bite him if he came too near. Then the ox said, "Why won't you let me eat my hay? It is no good to you. You can't eat it."

"I don't care," said the dog. "If I can't eat it, nobody else will either."

Selfishness is very stupid.

THE BOY AND THE NIGHTINGALE

One summer night, a boy asked a nightingale to sing. But the bird was already done with its song.

"Oh, my," said the nightingale. "I just don't feel like singing. The frogs are making too much noise. Don't you hear them?"

"Yes," said the boy, "I do hear them—but only because you are silent."

If someone is rude, we can often hide it by being kind.

THE TYRANT WHO BECAME JUST

Long ago there lived a king. He was so cruel that his people called him The Tyrant. (This means cruel master.) And they prayed for a new king. Then one day they were surprised. Their king called them together and said:

"My dear people, I will no longer be a cruel King. From now on you will be happy. I am going to try to rule justly and well."

The king kept his word. Soon he was known as The Just King. Then one of his favorites came to him and said:

"Please tell me how you had this change of heart toward your people?"

And the king said:

"One day I was riding. I saw a dog chasing a fox. The fox got away. But the dog had bitten his leg. It was a terrible bite. The fox would never be well again. Then the dog went home. And he met a man who threw a stone at him. The stone broke the dog's leg. The man walked on. He did not get far when a horse kicked him and broke his leg. The horse started to run. But he fell into a hole and broke his leg. When I saw these things I promised to become just and kind.

When people are cruel, they can expect cruel things to happen to them.

THE MAN WHO GAVE UP SINGING

A happy shoemaker sang at his work all day long. But he lived near a rich man. The rich man did not like the singing. He tried to think of a way to stop it. This is what he did.

He asked the shoemaker how much money he made in one year.

"Oh," said the shoemaker, "not more than fifty dollars. But I am quite happy."

"Very well," said the rich man. "Here is a present for you." He gave the man one hundred dollars.

The shoemaker was very happy. He had never had so much money in his life!

He thought about what he would do with it. Then he began to fear he might lose it. Soon his fear was great. He stopped singing at his work. And he became one of the most unhappy men in the village.

Money does not always bring happiness.

THE STAG AND THE WATER

One day a stag stood by the side of a pond. He looked at himself in the water. "My antlers are so beautiful!" he said. "They are so long and graceful. I wish the rest of my body was as nice. But look at my ugly legs! They are so thin. I don't like them at all."

Just then he heard some dogs. He could hear the hunters on their horses. He ran away. His long legs jumped over the branches and dead trees. Soon he had left the dogs and the men far behind. Then he went into the woods to hide. But his antlers got caught on some branches. He pulled and turned. But he could not get away.

As the hunters came closer, he said, "What a fool I was! My antlers made me so proud. Now they will cause my death. I thought my legs were so ugly. But they were the only things that could have saved me."

Sometimes the things we like most are not good for us. And something we don't like, we need.

THE FOX AND THE CROW

A hungry fox saw a crow. The crow was sitting in a tree. He had a piece of cheese in his mouth.

"You are the best crow I ever saw," said the fox. "I wish you would sing. A beautiful bird always has a good voice. And it is a long time since I have heard fine music."

The silly crow was very proud at being asked to sing. So he opened his mouth. The cheese fell out. The fox picked it up. As he went away he said, "I said that he is beautiful. But I did not say he is wise."

Do not be fooled by fine talk.

WHY THE WOLF WAS BRAVE

One day a wolf met a fox. He said, "My father was very brave. He killed more than 200 enemies in his life. I don't understand it. In the end, he was killed by only one enemy."

"You forget," said the fox. "The 200 enemies were only sheep. The first time he tried to get a bull, he was killed."

It is easy for the strong to hurt the weak.

THE MAN AND THE PEARS

A man was invited to a wedding in another town. As he walked along the road he saw some pears. They were beside the path. The man was hungry enough to eat them. But he did not want to. He was looking forward to the wonderful food at the wedding. So he kicked the pears into the ditch.

A little while later the man had to cross a small river. But it had rained so much that the little bridge was washed away. There were no boats around.

So at last the man had to give up all

hope of getting across. He turned around to go home. And now he was very hungry. When he saw the pears in the ditch, he was glad to pull them out and eat them.

Don't be took quick not to like things you think you don't need. Someday you may be glad to have them.

THE ANT AND THE GRASSHOPPER

A nest of ants had been busy all summer and fall. They were finding food for the winter. They put the food in the wonderful rooms they had built under the ground. So when winter came, they had plenty to eat.

One cold day a grasshopper came to the anthill. He was very hungry. He asked the ants to give him a little food.

One of the ants said, "How did you spend your time this summer? Did you save any food for the winter?"

The grasshopper said, "I spent all my time singing, playing, and dancing. I did not think about the winter."

The ant said, "Then we have nothing to give you. You played all summer. So you must expect to be hungry in the winter."

Put something away for when you may need it.

POETRY PATCHWORK

THE BLIND MEN AND
THE ELEPHANT

It was six men of Indostan
To learning much inclined,
Who went to see the elephant,
(Though all of them were blind),
That each by observation
Might satisfy his mind.

The first approached the elephant,
And happening to fall
Against his broad and sturdy side,
At once began to bawl:
"God bless me! but the elephant
Is very like a wall!"

The second, feeling of the tusk,
Cried: "Ho! what have we here
So very round and smooth and sharp?
To me 'tis mighty clear
This wonder of the elephant
Is very like a spear!"

The third approached the animal,
And happening to take
The squirming trunk within his hands,
Thus boldly up and spake:
"I see," quoth he, "the elephant
Is very like a snake!"

The fourth reached out his eager hand
And felt about the knee.
"What most this wondrous beast is
        like
Is mighty plain," quoth he;
" 'Tis clear enough the elephant
Is very like a tree!"

The fifth, who chanced to touch the
        ear,
Said: "E'en the blinest man
Can tell what this resembles most;
Deny the fact who can,
This marvel of an elephant
Is very like a fan!"

The sixth no sooner had begun
About the beast to grope
Than, seizing on the swinging tail
That fell within his scope,
"I see," quoth he, "the elephant
Is very like a rope!"

And so these men of Indostan
Disputed loud and long,
Each in his own opinion
Exceeding stiff and strong,
Though each was partly in the right,
And all were in the wrong!

John Godfrey Saxe

I'M NOBODY! WHO ARE YOU?

I'm Nobody! Who are you?
Are you—Nobody—Too?
Then there's a pair of us!
Don't tell! they'd banish us—you
      know!

How dreary—to be—Somebody!
How public—like a Frog—
To tell your name—the livelong
      June—
To an admiring Bog!

Emily Dickinson

SALT, MUSTARD, VINEGAR, PEPPER

Salt, Mustard, Vinegar, Pepper,
French almond rock,
Bread and butter for your supper
That's all mother's got.
Fish and chips and coca cola,
Put them in a pan,
Irish stew and ice cream soda,
We'll eat all we can.

Salt, Mustard, Vinegar, Pepper,
French almond rock,
Bread and butter for your supper
That's all mother's got.
Eggs and bacon, salted herring,
Put them in a pot,
Pickled onions, apple pudding,
We will eat the lot.

Salt, Mustard, Vinegar, Pepper,
Pig's head and trout,
Bread and butter for your supper
O U T spells out.

TRADITIONAL ENGLISH

POEMS ABOUT NATURE

I SHALL SING

Fall, leaves, fall; die, flowers, away;
Lengthen night and shorten day;
Every leaf speaks bliss to me
Fluttering from the autumn tree.

I shall smile when wreaths of snow
Blossom where the rose should grow;
I shall sing when night's decay
Ushers in a drearier day.

Emily Brontë

WEATHERS

This is the weather the cuckoo likes,
  And so do I;
When showers betumble the chestnut
    spikes,
  And nestlings fly:
And little brown nightingale bills his
    best,
And they sit outside "The Travellers'
    Rest",
And maids come forth sprig-muslin
    drest,
And citizens dream of the south and
    west,
  And so do I.

This is the weather the shepherd shuns,
  And so do I;
When beeches drip in browns and duns,
  And thresh, and ply;
And hill-hid tides throb, throe on throe,
And meadow rivulets overflow,
And drops on gate-bars hang in a row,
And rooks in families homeward go,
  And so do I.

                        Thomas Hardy

WHO HAS SEEN THE WIND?

Who has seen the wind?
  Neither I nor you?
But when the leaves hang trembling
  The wind is passing through.

Who has seen the wind?
  Neither you nor I:
But when the trees bow down their
    heads
  The wind is passing by.

                    Christina Rossetti

SEEDS

The seeds I sowed—
For weeks unseen—
Have pushed up pygmy
Shoots of green;
So frail you'd think
The tiniest stone
Would never let
A glimpse be shown.
But no; a pebble
Near them lies,
At least a cherry-stone
In size,
Which that mere sprout
Has heaved away,
To bask in sunshine,
See the day.

                    Walter de la Mare

I'LL TELL YOU HOW
THE SUN ROSE

I'll tell you how the sun rose,—
A ribbon at a time.
The steeples swam in amethyst,
The news like squirrels ran.

The hills untied their bonnets,
The bobolinks begun.
Then I said softly to myself,
"That must have been the sun!"

But how he set, I know not.
There seemed a purple stile
Which little yellow boys and girls
Were climbing all the while

Till when they reached the other side,
A dominie in gray
Put gently up the evening bars,
And led the flock away.

                    Emily Dickinson

THINGS THAT GO BUMP IN THE NIGHT

SHADOW MARCH

All round the house is the jet-black
    night;
    It stares through the window-pane;
It crawls in the corners, hiding from the
    light,
    And it moves with the moving flame.

Now my little heart goes a-beating like a
    drum,
    With the breath of the Bogie in my
      hair;
And all round the candle the crooked
    shadows come,
    And go marching along up the stair.

The shadow of the balusters, the shadow
    of the lamp,
    The shadow of the child that goes to
      bed—
All the wicked shadows coming, tramp,
    tramp, tramp,
    With the black night overhead.
               Robert Louis Stevenson

A SCOTTISH PRAYER

From ghoulies and ghosties and
    long-leggety beasties
And things that go bump in the night,
Good lord, deliver us!
               ANONYMOUS

335

WITCHES' CHARMS

The owl is abroad, the bat and the
  toad,
  And so is the cat-a-mountain;
The aunt and the mole sit both in a hole,
  And the frog peeps out of the fountain.
The dogs they do bay, and the timbrels
  play,
  The spindle is now a-turning;
The moon it is red, and the stars are fled,
  But the sky is a-burning.

The weather is fair, the wind is good
Up, dame, on your horse of wood!
Or else tuck up your grey frock,
And saddle your goat or your green
  cock,
And make his bridle a ball of thread
To roll up how many miles you have rid.
Quickly come away,
For we all stay.

Ben Jonson

THE BROOMSTICK TRAIN

Look out! Look out boys! Clear the
  track!
The witches are here! They've all
  come back!

They hanged them high—No use! No
  use!
What cares a switch for a hangman's
  noose?
They buried them deep but they
  wouldn't lie still,
For cats and witches are hard to kill;
They swore they shouldn't and
  wouldn't die—
Books said they did, but they lie! they
  lie!

Oliver Wendell Holmes

THE WITCH

I saw her plucking cowslips,
  And marked her where she stood:
She never knew I watched her
  While hiding in the wood.

Her skirt was brightest crimson,
  And black her steeple hat,
Her broomstick lay beside her—
  I'm positive of that.

Her chin was sharp and pointed,
  Her eyes were—I don't know—
For, when she turned towards me—
  I thought it best—to go!

Percy H. Ilot

336

NONSENSE RHYMES

YOU ARE OLD, FATHER WILLIAM

"You are old, Father William," the
    young man said,
"And your hair has become very white;
  And yet you incessantly stand on your
    head—
  Do you think, at your age, it is right?"

"In my youth," Father William replied
    to his son,
"I feared it might injure the brain;
  But now that I'm perfectly sure I have
    none,
  Why I do it again and again."

"You are old," said the youth, "as I
    mentioned before,
And have grown most uncommonly fat;
  Yet you turned a back-somersault in at
    the door—
  Pray, what is the reason of that?"

"In my youth," said the sage, as he shook
    his grey locks,
"I kept all my limbs very supple
  By the use of this ointment—one
    shilling the box—
  Allow me to sell you a couple?"

"You are old," said the youth, "and your
    jaws are too weak
For anything tougher than suet;
  Yet you finished the goose, with the
    bones and the beak—
  Pray, how did you manage to do it?"

"In my youth," said his father, "I took
    to the law,
And argued each case with my wife;
  And the muscular strength, which it
    gave to my jaw,
  Has lasted the rest of my life."

"You are old," said the youth, "one
    would hardly suppose
That your eye was as steady as ever;
  Yet you balanced an eel on the end of
    your nose—
  What made you so awfully clever?"

"I have answered three questions, and
    that is enough,"
Said the father; "don't give yourself
    airs!
Do you think I can listen all day to such
    stuff?
Be off, or I'll kick you down stairs!"
             Lewis Carroll

ONE BRIGHT MORNING

One bright morning in the middle of
  the night
Two dumb boys got up to fight.
Back to back they faced each other,
Drew their swords and shot each other.
A deaf policeman heard the noise,
Came and arrested those two dumb
  boys.

TRADITIONAL AMERICAN

THE COMMON CORMORANT

The common cormorant or shag
Lays eggs inside a paper bag
The reason you will see no doubt
It is to keep the lightning out
But what these unobservant birds
Have never noticed is that herds
Of wandering bears may come with
  buns
And steal the bags to hold the crumbs.

THE OWL AND THE PUSSY-CAT

The Owl and the Pussy-Cat went to sea
  In a beautiful pea-green boat,
They took some honey, and plenty of
  money
  Wrapped up in a five-pound note.
The Owl looked up to the stars above,
  And sang to a small guitar.
"O lovely Pussy, O Pussy, my love,
  What a beautiful Pussy you are,
      You are,
      You are!
  What a beautiful Pussy you are!"

Pussy said to the Owl, "You elegant
  fowl,
  How charmingly sweet you sing!
Oh! let us be married, too long we have
  tarried:

But what shall we do for a ring?"
They sailed away for a year and a day,
  To the land where the Bong-tree
    grows;
And there in a wood a Piggy-wig stood,
  With a ring at the end of his nose,
      His nose,
      His nose,
  With a ring at the end of his nose.

"Dear pig, are you willing to sell for
    one shilling
  Your ring?" Said the Piggy, "I will."
So they took it away, and were married
    next day
  By the Turkey who lives on the hill.
They dined on mince and slices of
    quince,
  Which they ate with a runcible spoon;
And hand in hand, on the edge of the
    sand,
  They danced by the light of the moon,
      The moon,
      The moon,
  They danced by the light of the moon.

Edward Lear

LADLES AND JELLYSPOONS

Ladles and jellyspoons:
I come before you
To stand behind you
And tell you something
I know nothing about.

Next Thursday,
The day after Friday,
There'll be a ladies' meeting
For men only.

Wear your best clothes
If you haven't any,
And if you can come
Please stay home.

Admission is free,
You can pay at the door.
We'll give you a seat
So you can sit on the floor.

It makes no difference
Where you sit;
The kid in the gallery
Is sure to spit.

TRADITIONAL ENGLISH

WILL YOU WALK A LITTLE FASTER?

"Will you walk a little faster?" said a
    whiting to a snail.
"There's a porpoise close behind us, and
    he's treading on my tail.
See how eagerly the lobsters and the
    turtles all advance!
They are waiting on the shingle—will
    you come and join the dance?
Will you, won't you, will you, won't
    you, will you join the dance?

Will you, won't you, will you, won't
    you, won't you join the dance?

"You can really have no notion how
    delightful it will be,
When they take us up and throw us,
    with the lobsters out to sea!"
But the snail replied 'Too far, too far!'
    and gave a look askance—
Said he thanked the whiting kindly, but
    he would not join the dance.
Would not, could not, would not, could
    not, would not join the dance.
Would not, could not, would not, could
    not, could not join the dance.

"What matters it how far we go?" his
    scaly friend replied.
"There is another shore, you know, upon
    the other side.
The further off from England the
    nearer is to France—
Then turn not pale, beloved snail, but
    come and join the dance.
Will you, won't you, will you, won't
    you, will you join the dance?
Will you, won't you, will you, won't
    you, won't you join the dance?"

Lewis Carroll

MY DREAM

I dreamed a dream next Tuesday week,
    Beneath the apple-trees;
I thought my eyes were big pork-pies,
    And my nose was Stilton cheese.
The clock struck twenty minutes to six,
    When a frog sat on my knee;
I asked him to lend me eighteenpence,
    But he borrowed a shilling off me.

JABBERWOCKY

'Twas brillig, and the slithy toves
  Did gyre and gimble in the wabe:
All mimsy were the borogroves,
  And the mome raths outgrabe.

"Beware the Jabberwock, my son!
  The jaws that bite, the claws that catch!
Beware the Jubjub bird, and shun
  The frumious Bandersnatch!"

He took his vorpal sword in hand:
Long time the manxome foe he
    sought—
So rested he by the Tumtum tree,
And stood awhile in thought.

And, as in uffish thought he stood,
The Jabberwock, with eyes of flame,
Came whiffling through the tulgey
    wood,
And burbled as it came!

One, two! One, two! And through and
    through
The vorpal blade went snicker-snack!
He left it dead, and with its head
He went galumphing back.

"And hast thou slain the Jabberwock?
  Come to my arms, my beamish boy!
O frabjous day! Callooh! Callay!"
  He chortled in his joy.

'Twas brillig, and the slithy toves
  Did gyre and gimble in the wabe:
All mimsy were the borogroves,
  And the mome raths outgrabe.
                            Lewis Carroll

THE MINISTER IN THE PULPIT

The minister in the pulpit,
He couldn't say his prayers,
He laughed and he giggled,
And he fell down the stairs.
The stairs gave a crack,
And he broke his humpy back,
And all the congregation
Went "Quack, quack, quack."
                  TRADITIONAL ENGLISH

340

A CHILD'S GARDEN OF VERSES

WHERE GO THE BOATS?

Dark brown is the river,
  Golden is the sand.
It flows along for ever
  With trees on either hand.

Green leaves a-floating,
  Castles of the foam,
Boats of mine a-boating—
  Where will all come home?

On goes the river
  And out past the mill,
Away down the valley,
  Away down the hill.

Away down the river,
  A hundred miles or more,
Other little children
  Shall bring my boats ashore.

BED IN SUMMER

In winter I get up at night
And dress by yellow candle-light.
In summer, quite the other way,
I have to go to bed by day.

I have to go to bed and see
The birds still hopping on the tree,
Or hear the grown-up people's feet
Still going past me in the street.

And does it not seem hard to you,
When all the sky is clear and blue,
And I should so much like to play,
To have to go to bed by day?

THE SWING

How do you like to go up in a swing?
  Up in the air so blue?
Oh, I do think it the pleasantest thing
  Ever a child can do!

Up in the air and over the wall,
  Till I can see so wide,
Rivers and trees and cattle and all
  Over the countryside—

Till I look down on the garden green,
  Down on the roof so brown—
Up in the air I go flying again,
  Up in the air and down!

THE LAND OF COUNTERPANE

When I was sick and lay a-bed,
I had two pillows at my head,
And all my toys beside me lay
To keep me happy all the day.

And sometimes for an hour or so
I watched my leaden soldiers go,
With different uniforms and drills,
Among the bed-clothes, through the
    hills;

And sometimes sent my ships in fleets
All up and down among the sheets;
Or brought my trees and houses out,
And planted cities all about.

I was the giant great and still
That sits upon the pillow-hill,
And sees before him, dale and plain,
The pleasant land of counterpane.

MY SHADOW

I have a little shadow that goes in and
    out with me,
And what can be the use of him is more
    than I can see.
He is very, very like me from the heels
    up to the head;
And I see him jump before me when I
    jump into my bed.

The funniest thing about him is the way
    he likes to grow—
Not at all like proper children, which is
    always very slow;
For he sometimes shoots up taller like an
    india-rubber ball,
And he sometimes gets so little that
    there's none of him at all.

He hasn't got a notion of how children
    ought to play,
And can only make a fool of me in every
    sort of way.
He stays so close beside me, he's a
    coward you can see;
I'd think shame to stick to nursie as that
    shadow sticks to me!

One morning, very early, before the sun
    was up
I rose and found the shining dew on
    every buttercup;
But my lazy little shadow, like an arrant
    sleepy-head,
Had stayed at home behind me and was
    fast asleep in bed.

POEMS ABOUT ANIMALS

THE EAGLE

He clasps the crag with crooked hands;
Close to the sun in lonely lands,
Ringed with the azure world, he stands.

The wrinkled sea beneath him crawls;
He watches from his mountain walls,
And like a thunderbolt he falls.
Alfred, Lord Tennyson

EARWIG

The horny goloch is an awesome beast,
Supple and scaly;
It has two horns, and a hantle of feet,
And a forkie tailie.

TRADITIONAL SCOTTISH

DOGS AND WEATHER

I'd like a different dog
    For every kind of weather—
A narrow greyhound for a fog,
    A wolfhound strange and white,
With a tail like a silver feather
    To run with in the night,
      When snow is still and winter stars are
      bright.

In the fall I'd like to see
    In answer to my whistle,
A golden spaniel look at me.
    But best of all for rain
A terrier, hairy as a thistle,
    To trot with fine disdain
    Beside me down the soaked,
      sweet-smelling lane.
Winifred Welles

A TALE

There was an old woman sat spinning,
And that's the first beginning;
She had a calf,
And that's a half;
She took it by the tail,
And threw it over the wall,
And that's all.

ANONYMOUS

MICE

I think mice
Are rather nice.

Their tails are long,
Their faces small,
They haven't any
Chins at all.
Their ears are pink,
Their teeth are white,
They run about
The house at night.
They nibble things
They shouldn't touch
And no one seems
To like them much.

But I think mice
Are nice.

Rose Fyleman

CATS

Cats sleep
Anywhere,
Any table,
Any chair,
Top of piano,
Window-ledge,
In the middle,
On the edge,
Open drawer,
Empty shoe,
Anybody's
Lap will do,
Fitted in a
Cardboard box,
In the cupboard
With your frocks—
Anywhere!
They don't care!
Cats sleep
Anywhere.

Eleanor Farjeon

THE FROG

What a wonderful bird the frog are!
When he stand he sit almost;
When he hop, he fly almost;
He ain't got no sense hardly;
He ain't got no tail hardly either.
When he sit, he sit on what he ain't got
    almost.

ANONYMOUS

THE NURSERY RHYMES

GEORGIE PORGIE

Georgie Porgie, pudding and pie,
Kissed the girls and made them cry;
When the boys came out to play,
Georgie Porgie ran away.

p.g.7

THE OLD WOMAN IN A SHOE

There was an old woman who lived in a shoe,
She had so many children she didn't know what to do;
She gave them some broth without any bread;
She whipped them all soundly and put them to bed.

p.g. 14 and 15

HUMPTY DUMPTY

Humpty Dumpty sat on a wall,
Humpty Dumpty had a great fall;
All the King's horses and all the King's men
Couldn't put Humpty together again.

JACK HORNER

Little Jack Horner
Sat in a corner,
Eating a Christmas pie;
He put in his thumb,
And pulled out a plum,
And said, What a good boy am I!

JACK AND JILL

Jack and Jill
Went up the hill,
To fetch a pail of water;
Jack fell down,
And broke his crown,
And Jill came tumbling after.

HEY DIDDLE, DIDDLE

Hey diddle, diddle,
The cat and the fiddle,
The cow jumped over the moon;
The little dog laughed
To see such sport,
And the dish ran away with the spoon.

MISS MUFFET

Little Miss Muffet
Sat on a tuffet,
Eating her curds and whey;
There came a big spider,
Who sat down beside her
And frightened Miss Muffet away.

P. 96

MARY'S LAMB

Mary had a little lamb,
Its fleece was white as snow;
And everywhere that Mary went
The lamb was sure to go.

It followed her to school one day,
That was against the rule;
It made the children laugh and play
To see a lamb at school.

P. 96
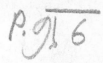

LULLABY

Rock-a-bye, baby, on the tree top,
When the wind blows the cradle will rock;
When the bough breaks the cradle will fall,
Down will come baby, cradle, and all.

347

pg. 0

BOY BLUE

Little Boy Blue, come blow your horn,
The sheep's in the meadow, the cow's in
  the corn;
But where is the boy who looks after the
  sheep?
He's under a haycock fast asleep.
Will you wake him? No, not I,
For if I do, he's sure to cry.

pg. 19

HICKORY, DICKORY, DOCK

Hickory, dickory, dock
The mouse ran up the clock;
The clock struck one,
The mouse ran down,
Hickory, dickory, dock.

348

BAA, BAA, BLACK SHEEP

Baa, Baa, black sheep, have you any wool?
Yes, sir, yes, sir, three bags full;
One for the master, and one for the dame,
And one for the little boy who lives down the lane.

PEASE PORRIDGE HOT

Pease porridge hot,
Pease porridge cold,
Pease porridge in the pot
Nine days old.
Some like it hot,
Some like it cold,
Some like it in the pot
Nine days old.

10 0 10 0 10.0
100 10 0 100
100 100 100
100 ⚹⚹⚹⚹⚹⚹⚹⚹⚹⚹
◡ ◡ ◡ ◡ ◡ ◡ ◡ ◡ ◡ ◡ ◡